Audio CD included

Navigate

Workbook
without key

B1 **Pre-intermediate**

OXFORD
UNIVERSITY PRESS

Contents

Oxford 3000™ *Navigate* has been based on the Oxford 3000 to ensure that learners are only covering the most relevant vocabulary.

Time

1.1 Do you live in the past, present or future?

Vocabulary daily life

1 What do you do? Match situations 1–8 to verb phrases a–h.

1	You need a holiday.	a	spend time with relatives
2	You go to a party.	b	do some work
3	It's raining.	c	eat healthy food and you'll feel better
4	Your boss arrives.	d	have fun
5	You're bored.	e	make a to-do list
6	It's your cousin's birthday.	f	stay in
7	You're ill.	g	go on a trip
8	You have a busy weekend.	h	chat with friends online

2 Complete the to-do list with the correct verbs.

THINGS TO DO

SATURDAY

1 _do_ housework

2 _____ the shopping (buy something for lunch!)

3 _____ some exercise (football 3 p.m.)

Go dancing – 4 _____ a good time!

5 _____ to bed late

SUNDAY

6 _____ a lie-in!

7 _____ a family meal

8 _____ future plans (holiday with family this year?)

9 _____ English homework

10 _____ an early night

3 Match verbs in A to phrases in B to make verb phrases. Then complete the information sheet.

A do ~~eat~~ go go have have spend stay

B an early night a good time ~~healthy food~~ in shopping some exercise time with relatives to bed late

TOP TIPS FOR STAYING HEALTHY

1 _Eat healthy food_

Doctors say we need to have seven pieces of fruit and vegetables every day. When you can, 2 _____ at a market and buy apples and tomatoes that are fresh.

3 _____

Doctors say the sun is good for us and we need to go out and walk or play sport. Don't 4 _____ all day in front of the TV – it's bad for you.

5 _____

Doctors say that we need eight hours' sleep every night. Don't 6 _____ when you need to get up early in the morning.

7 _____ **and friends**

Doctors say that happy people live for a long time. Go out and 8 _____ two or three times every week. It isn't good for you to be always on your own.

Grammar question forms

4a Complete the conversations with the question words in the box.

> how many   how much   how often   what kind
> ~~what time~~   when   where   who

1 A _What time_ do you get up during the week?
   B At half past seven.
2 A _____ is the first person you see every morning?
   B My brother. He gets up at the same time as me.
3 A _____ do you have breakfast?
   B In the kitchen.
4 A _____ coffee do you drink?
   B I have three or four cups a day.
5 A _____ do you stop for lunch?
   B From one o'clock until two.
6 A _____ do you eat in a restaurant?
   B About twice a month.
7 A _____ good friends do you have?
   B A lot. I have a lot of good friends.
8 A _____ of car do you drive?
   B I drive a Mini.

b **1.1**))) Listen and check.

c **1.1**))) Listen again. Pause the CD and repeat after each question.

5a Insert the word in brackets in the correct place in the sentences.

1 When your birthday? (is) _When is your birthday?_
2 Who you chat with online? (do)
3 What kind films do you like? (of)
4 Are busy right now? (you)
5 How do you spend time with relatives? (often)
6 How many did you sleep last night? (hours)
7 Where you from? (are)
8 You go shopping yesterday? (did)

b **1.2**))) Listen and check.

c **1.2**))) Listen again. Pause the CD and repeat after each question.

6 Complete the questions in the conversation with question words and the verbs in brackets.

A Hi. It's nice to meet you. ¹ _Are you_ (be) new?
B Yes, I am. My name's Laila.
A I'm Sally. ² _____ _____ _____ (have) fun tonight?
B Yes, I did. It was a great class.
A ³ _____ _____ _____ _____ (start) playing tennis?
B Years ago. I was about ten, I think.
A ⁴ _____ _____ (be) good at it?
B Well ... I won some competitions last year.
A How ⁵ _____ _____ _____ _____ (win) ?
B Three or four.
A Congratulations! Laila, ⁶ _____ _____ _____ (live) near here?
B No, I live in the town centre.
A Me, too. ⁷ _____ _____ _____ _____ (get) here today?
B I came by bus.
A This is my car. ⁸ _____ _____ _____ (want) to go home together?
B Yes! Thanks a lot.
A No problem.

I can ...	Very well	Quite well	More practice
talk about my daily life.	○	○	○
ask questions.	○	○	○

1.2 Free time

Grammar present simple and adverbs of frequency

1a Put the words in the right order to make sentences.

1 often / coffee / for / go / They / out / a
They often go out for a coffee.

2 goes / My / and / running / then / every / girlfriend / now

3 don't / the / usually / We / camping / in / go / summer

4 best / aerobics / a / friend / My / twice / week / or / does / once

5 ever / games / I / play / hardly / computer

6 family / often / My / future / don't / plans / make

b **1.3**))) Listen and check. Notice which words and parts of words are stressed.

c **1.3**))) Listen again. Pause the CD and repeat after each word.

2 Complete the second sentence so that it means the same as the first. Replace the **bold** words with the adverbs and expressions in the box.

always   every now and then   most days
once or twice a year   rarely

1 My partner does exercise after work **every day**.
My partner _always does exercise_ after work.

2 They **hardly ever** have a lie-in because they have two small children.
They _____ because they have two small children.

3 My sister **nearly always** goes on Facebook before she has breakfast.
_____ before she has breakfast.

4 My parents go on holiday **in January and July or only in July**.
My parents _____.

5 We **occasionally** go clubbing with a big group of friends.
_____ with a big group of friends.

3 Complete the article with the verb phrases and the adverbs in the box.

always   ~~hardly ever~~   nearly always   never   occasionally
often   sometimes   usually

	Mon	Tues	Weds	Thurs	Fri	Sat	Sun
eat healthily	✓	✓	✓	✓	✓	✓	✓
go training	✓	✓	✓	✓	✓	✓	
be in bed by 11 p.m.	✓	✓	✓	✓	✓		
chat with friends online	✓		✓		✓		✓
watch videos		✓		✓		✓	
spend time with relatives							✓
have a lie-in							✓
be bored							

A week in the life of an Olympic athlete

Olympic athletes have to look after their health if they want to be the best. In the morning, they [1] _hardly ever have_ a lie-in because they have a lot of things to do – a sports star [2] _____ bored! In general, athletes [3] _____ and they start the day with a big breakfast with lots of carbohydrates and protein. They [4] _____ training in the morning and again in the evening. After training, they [5] _____ of other athletes to see how good they are. Olympic athletes don't have a lot of time to see other people, but they [6] _____ at the weekend – having a meal or catching up on family news. They [7] _____ or by phone. Professional athletes need between eight and ten hours sleep every night, so they [8] _____ in bed by 11 p.m.

Vocabulary free-time activities

4 Write phrases for the photos with the words in the box and *play, do* or *go*.

aerobics ~~basketball~~ camping cards clubbing on Facebook to the gym yoga

1 play basketball

2

3

4

5

6

7

8

5 Circle the incorrect phrase.

1 GO (aerobics) for a walk on Facebook running
2 PLAY basketball chess computer games swimming
3 DO exercise golf karate yoga
4 GO basketball camping out for a coffee to the gym
5 PLAY cards football golf karate
6 GO clubbing exercise out for a meal swimming

6 Complete the advert with *play, do* or *go* and the words and phrases in the box.

~~computer games~~ exercise football for a meal for a walk golf running swimming

Come to **CenterParcs**

Looking for a perfect family holiday?

CenterParcs is not the place to go if you want to ¹ _play computer games_ all day. But it <u>is</u> right for you if you're looking for some action! Here are some of the exciting activities you can do:

▶ ²_____ in our outdoor pool. The pool is heated to 29.5°C so it isn't cold.

▶ ³_____ in our fitness classes. There are Zumba classes for all the family!

▶ ⁴_____ on our 18-hole course. You're sure to have a good time.

▶ ⁵_____ in the forest and learn more about nature. If you have more energy, you can ⁶_____ early in the morning when everybody is asleep.

▶ send your children to ⁷_____. Our coach will teach them for an hour before they play a match together.

▶ after all the excitement, ⁸_____ in one of our many restaurants. It's a great time to relax!

For more information, contact us by phone or on our website.

I can ...	Very well	Quite well	More practice
talk about how often I do things.	○	○	○
talk about my free time.	○	○	○

1.3 Vocabulary development

Vocabulary nouns and verbs with the same form

1 Complete the conversations with the words in the box. Use the correct form of the same word for each conversation.

> dream experience ~~photograph~~ plan post promise text

1 **A** Do you take many _photographs_ ?
  B No, I only _photograph_ things that interest me.
2 **A** Who do you tell first if you have a bad _____?
  B If I _____ something awful, I always tell my best friend.
3 **A** Do you make a _____ for the week every Monday morning?
  B Yes, I _____ exactly what I'm going to do.
4 **A** Do you often have the same _____ every night?
  B Yes, I _____ that I am falling into a dark hole.
5 **A** Do you usually call your friends or do you write a _____?
  B I always _____ them before we go out.
6 **A** Do you always think hard before you make a _____?
  B No. I often _____ to phone my parents and then I forget.
7 **A** Do you often write a _____ on Facebook?
  B No, but I often _____ music videos.

2 Complete the article with the correct form of some of the words in exercise 1.

> Mobile phones can do more things today than ever before. Of course, you can use them to make calls and write [1] _texts_ , but they are also great for taking [2]_____. A phone camera is better than a digital camera because it is always with you. You don't usually [3]_____ to photograph something when you leave home, but if you see something interesting or have an unusual [4]_____, you can take out your phone and [5]_____ it. Today, you can also have more fun with your photos. In the past, you put a photo on your computer, and you hardly ever had a look at it again. But now, you can go on Facebook and [6]_____ your photos on your profile. You can also publish them on a blog. With all of this new technology, we can do things that people didn't [7]_____ of in the past.

Vocabulary review

→ **STUDY TIP** When you come across new verb phrases, record them under the verb in your notebooks. This will make it easier for you to learn them.

3 Complete the table with the phrases in the box.

> ~~a family meal~~ a good time a lie-in a to-do list an early night fun future plans healthy food homework housework in on a trip shopping some exercise some work the shopping time with relatives to bed late with friends online

chat	do	eat	go

have	make	spend	stay
a family meal			

4 Complete the table with the headings in the box.

> do go play

1_____	2_____	3_____
camping	cards	aerobics
clubbing	chess	exercise
for a walk	computer games	karate
on Facebook	football	yoga
out for coffee/a meal	golf	
running	basketball	
swimming		
to the gym		

5 Complete the table with the correct headings.

1_____	2_____	3_____
a look	a photograph	a film
an experience		a record
a dream		a promise

1.4   Speaking and writing

Speaking talking about the weather

1   Complete the conversation with the words in the box.

~~damp~~ humid mild pleasant showers thunderstorm

A   What's the weather like where you are?
B   It's raining today, so everything is ¹ _damp_ .
A   Does it rain a lot in your area?
B   It doesn't usually rain all day, but we often have a few
     ² _____.
A   What's it like in the summer?
B   It isn't very ³_____, because it gets very hot
     and ⁴_____. Occasionally, there's a ⁵_____
     in the evening, which can be quite frightening.
A   What's your favourite season?
B   I like the spring. It's nearly always very ⁶_____,
     and you can go out without a coat.

Speaking talking about likes and dislikes

2a   Complete the second sentence so that it means the same
     as the first, using the word in brackets.
     1   I like going clubbing a lot. (love)
          I _love going clubbing._____
     2   I hate the winter. (stand)
          I _____
     3   I like doing yoga a lot. (into)
          I _____
     4   I like basketball more than any other sport. (favourite)
          My _____

5   Doing housework isn't a problem for me. (mind)
     I _____
6   I don't like thunderstorms. (keen)
     I _____
7   Going camping is OK, I suppose. (quite)
     I _____
8   I like football more than golf. (prefer)
     I _____
9   I like doing karate a lot. (interested)
     I _____

PRONUNCIATION sentence stress

b   **1.4**))) Listen and check. Notice which words and parts of the
     words are stressed.

c   **1.4**))) Listen again. Pause the CD and repeat after each word.

Writing a web post about the best time to
visit your country

3   Complete the web post with *and*, *but* or *so*.

Suzanne Fischer

My family and I would like to visit Rio de Janeiro,
Brazil. When is the best time to go?

Paulo

The most popular time to visit Rio is from
December to March. This is our summer season
¹ _but_ it sometimes rains. The weather is usually
nice and warm, ² _____ the sun can be very
dangerous. You need to use cream when you go
outside ³ _____ it's safer to stay inside in the
middle of the day.

The city is always busy in the summer ⁴ _____
it can be very expensive. ⁵ _____ the best
time to come is in spring or autumn when flights
are cheaper ⁶ _____ there are fewer tourists.

Have a good trip!

I can ...	Very well	Quite well	More practice
understand and use nouns and verbs with the same form.	○	○	○
talk about the weather, my likes and dislikes.	○	○	○
write a web post.	○	○	○

2

Inside outside

2.1 Street life

Vocabulary street life

1 Choose the correct option to complete the sentences.
   1 Ellis Island isn't *dirty /* huge */ safe*, but there's an important statue on it.
   2 The bus is *crowded / dull / safe*. There are a lot of passengers.
   3 It's a *dirty / dull / lively* market. There are a lot of stalls.
   4 The beach is *crowded / huge / safe*. You can swim in the sea.
   5 The park is *dirty / huge / lively*. There's a lot of rubbish.
   6 It's a *crowded / dull / lively* area. There's nothing to do.

2 Match words in column A to words in column B to make compound nouns. Then match the compound nouns to the definitions 1–7.

A	B
street	area
parking	cleaner
souvenir	artist
pavement	performer
market	place
pedestrian	space
street	seller

   1 A person who picks up the rubbish. *street cleaner*
   2 A place where cars can't go. _____
   3 A person who has a stall with things for tourists. _____
   4 A place where there are a lot of stalls. _____
   5 A person who draws pictures on the street. _____
   6 A place where you can leave your car. _____
   7 A person who acts or sings outside. _____

3 Complete the article with the words in exercises **1** and **2**.

Famous city squares

Djemaa el Fna is a **1** *lively* square full of energy in the centre of Marrakech in Morocco. This is a **2**_____ _____ with no cars, so the best way to go there is on foot. During the day, the square is a **3**_____ _____ where people go shopping. There are all kinds of **4**_____, selling everything from carpets to spices. You can see **5**_____ _____, such as dancers and story tellers, and you can buy presents to take home from the **6**_____ _____. The market fills all the narrow streets around the square, so it is absolutely **7**_____. The busiest time of day is late afternoon when the market is very **8**_____. The square is quite **9** _____ as there are police officers on every corner. At the end of the evening, the square is very **10**_____ and there is a lot of **11**_____ on the streets. In the early morning, it's time for the **12**_____ _____ to start work and prepare the square for the next day.

PRONUNCIATION word stress in street life words

4a Underline the syllable we stress in these words.
   1 <u>clea</u>ner   6 pedestrian
   2 crowded   7 performer
   3 lively   8 rubbish
   4 market   9 souvenir
   5 pavement   10 statue

b **2.1**))) Listen and check.

c **2.1**))) Listen again. Pause the CD and repeat after each word.

Grammar present simple and present continuous

5a Complete the sentences with the present continuous form of the verbs in the box. Use contractions where possible.

> celebrate do not feel ~~have~~ run not talk wait not watch

1 We're tired. We _'re having_ an early night.
2 My husband is late for work. He _____ out of the door.
3 You can turn the TV off. I _____ it.
4 Your dog is hungry. It _____ by the cupboard.
5 Can you help me? I _____ my English homework.
6 My sisters are angry. They _____ to each other.
7 Robert is in bed. He _____ very well.
8 My grandfather is 80 today. We _____ his birthday with him.

PRONUNCIATION contractions in present continuous

b 2.2))) Listen and check.

c 2.2))) Listen again. Pause the CD and repeat after each word.

6 Choose the correct options to complete the conversations.
1 **A** Where *do you go / are you going*?
   B To the shops. *Do you want / Are you wanting* anything?
2 **A** *Do you listen / Are you listening* to the radio at the moment?
   B Yes, I *like / 'm liking* this programme.
3 **A** What *do you do / are you doing* on Saturday evenings?
   B I usually *go / 'm going* out.
4 **A** What time *does the market open / is the market opening*?
   B I *don't know / 'm not knowing*, sorry.
5 **A** *Does your partner / Is your partner working* today?
   B No, he *doesn't work / isn't working* on Fridays.
6 **A** *Do you have / Are you having* fun?
   B Yes, I *have / 'm having* a great time.
7 **A** *Do I need / Am I needing* an umbrella?
   B No, it *doesn't rain / isn't raining*.
8 **A** *Is our team winning / Does our team win*?
   B No, they *play / 're playing* really badly today.

7 Rewrite the sentences with the correct time expression in brackets.
1 I make a to-do list. (never/nowadays)
   I never make a to-do list.
2 My parents have a family meal. (every Sunday/now)
   _____
3 We're eating healthy food. (usually/these days)
   _____
4 My partner is doing some work. (occasionally/at the moment)
   _____
5 Luca goes to bed late. (always/now)
   _____
6 I'm chatting with friends online. (often/right now)
   _____

8 Complete the article with the correct present simple or present continuous form of the verbs in brackets.

Fabulous La Rambla

One of the most famous streets in the world is La Rambla in Barcelona, Spain. La Rambla ¹ _starts_ (start) in the Plaça de Catalunya, a huge square in the centre of the city, and ² _____ (finish) at the statue of Christopher Columbus in the port. The street ³ _____ (have) a central pedestrian area and it ⁴ _____ (get) very crowded at the weekend.

Today is a typical day in La Rambla and the street is full of tourists. Some people ⁵ _____ (sit) at pavement cafés and others ⁶ _____ (watch) the street performers. A local woman ⁷ _____ (buy) some flowers from a stall and an American tourist ⁸ _____ (look) at postcards at a souvenir seller's. He ⁹ _____ (want) to write to his friends back home.

Most people ¹⁰ _____ (like) going to La Rambla because there is so much to do and see there, and it ¹¹ _____ (become) one of the most important parts of Barcelona. These days more tourists ¹² _____ (spend) time there than ever before.

I can ...	Very well	Quite well	More practice
talk about where I live.	○	○	○
talk about the present.	○	○	○

2.2 Home life

1 Choose the correct options to complete the article.

Making igloos

The Inuit are a group of people ¹(*that*) / *where* / *which* live north of the Arctic Circle. Nunavut is the name of the area ²*where* / *which* / *who* they live in Canada. It is a place ³*where* / *which* / *who* the temperature often goes down to -40°C. The Inuit sometimes build igloos to protect themselves from the cold when they are hunting animals. An igloo is a round house ⁴*that* / *where* / *who* is made out of snow. There are Inuits ⁵*where* / *which* / *who* can build an igloo in less than an hour. They use snow ⁶*where* / *which* / *who* is very hard, and they cut it into squares. Inside an igloo, it can be 16°C when it is well below freezing outside.

2a Complete the definitions with *where*, *which* or *who*. Then match them to the words in the box.

> ball   dentist   DVD   garage   kitchen   ~~neighbour~~   picture
> police officer

1 It's a person __who__ lives in the house next to you. __neighbour__
2 It's the place _____ you keep your car. _____
3 It's a thing _____ you put on the wall. _____
4 It's a thing _____ you watch when there's nothing on TV. _____
5 It's the person _____ looks after your teeth. _____
6 It's a thing _____ you use to do sport. _____
7 It's the place _____ you make lunch. _____
8 It's a person _____ keeps you safe. _____

b In which sentences in exercise **2a** could *where*, *which* or *who* be replaced by *that*?

3 Join the two sentences to make one sentence. Use *where*, *which* or *who*.
1 They're shoes. I wear them to go running.
   They're the shoes __which I wear to go running.__
2 That's a phone. I use it for work.
   That's the phone _____
3 He's a mechanic. He repairs my car.
   He's the mechanic _____
4 That's a chair. My grandfather always sits there.
   That's the chair _____
5 She's a hairdresser. She cuts my hair.
   She's the hairdresser _____
6 That's a bus. It goes to the city centre.
   That's the bus _____
7 That's a supermarket. We do our shopping there.
   That's the supermarket _____

4a Underline the words that are stressed.
1 It's <u>something</u> that you <u>have</u> in your <u>house</u>.
2 It's something that you turn on and off.
3 It's something that has water in it.

b 2.3 ⟫ Listen and check.

c 2.3 ⟫ Listen again. Pause the CD and repeat after each word.

Vocabulary   household objects

5 Match words in box A to words in box B to make household objects. Then complete the sentences.

A   chest   ~~dish~~   dustpan   microwave   satellite   wash

B   basin   and brush   of drawers   oven   TV   ~~washer~~

1   A _dishwasher_ is a machine that cleans dirty plates and glasses.
2   A _____ _____ _____ are things that you use to clean the floor with.
3   The place where you usually clean your teeth is the _____ _____.
4   A machine where you can make food hot again is a _____ _____.
5   _____ _____ lets people watch programmes from all over the world.
6   The place where you keep some of your clothes is a _____ _____ _____.

6 Complete the crossword by looking at the photos.

```
        1
        C
        A
2 _ _ R _ _ _          3 _
        P
4 _ _ E _   5 _       6 _
        T
            7 _ _ 8 _ _ _
```

7 Complete the sentences with some of the words in exercises **5** and **6**.

1   Your hair looks awful. Look in the _mirror_ .
2   The _____ is dirty because of your shoes. Please take them off.
3   I want to have a shower. Can I borrow a _____?
4   Your shirts are clean. Please hang them up in the _____.
5   I dropped my toast. Where can I find a _____?
6   The meal was delicious. Let me put the plates in the _____ for you.

I can …	Very well	Quite well	More practice
identify things and people.	○	○	○
talk about things in my home.	○	○	○

2.3 Vocabulary development

Vocabulary phrases with *on*

1 Match definitions 1–8 to phrases in the box.

> on business   on holiday   on public transport   ~~on the internet~~
> on the left   on the way   on time   on TV

1 online   *on the internet*
2 during the journey   _____
3 opposite direction to 'on the right'   _____
4 at the beach   _____
5 you can watch it on the television   _____
6 not late   _____
7 on the metro, on a bus or on a tram   _____
8 doing work activities   _____

2 Complete the conversations with the phrases with *on* in exercise **1**.

1 **A** Can you buy some bread _*on the way*_ home?
  B Yes, of course. No problem.
2 **A** Where's your partner?
  B He's away _____. He has an important meeting in Brussels.
3 **A** How do I get to your house?
  B Walk down Princess Street towards the church and it's _____.
4 **A** Do you want to go by car?
  B No. Let's go _____. It's quicker.
5 **A** Aren't your parents at home?
  B No, they're _____ in Majorca.

Vocabulary review

3 Complete the table with the words in the box.

> ~~crowded~~   market place   pavement artist   safe   statue
> street performer

Adjectives to describe your town	People in the street	Places and things in the street
1 *crowded*	3 _____	5 _____
dirty	souvenir seller	parking space
dull	street cleaner	pedestrian area
huge	4 _____	rubbish
lively		stall
2 _____		6 _____

STUDY TIP
When you can, try to record new vocabulary in groups. A mind map is a great way of doing this and the new words will be easier to learn.

4 Complete the mind map with the headings in the box.

> things in the kitchen   things to clean with
> ~~things in the bedroom~~   things in the sitting room
> things to light when it gets dark   things in the bathroom

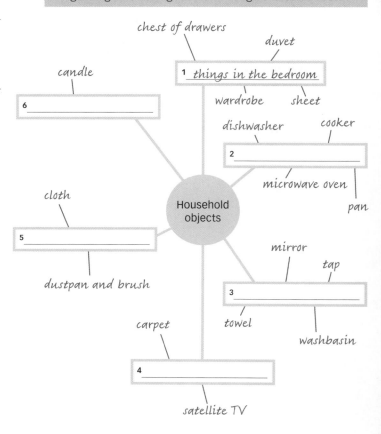

chest of drawers
duvet
candle
1 *things in the bedroom*
wardrobe   sheet
6 _____
dishwasher   cooker
2 _____
microwave oven
cloth
Household objects
pan
5 _____
mirror
tap
dustpan and brush
3 _____
carpet   towel
washbasin
4 _____
satellite TV

5 Complete the table with the phrases in the box.

> on the way   ~~checking news and information on the computer~~
> on business   positioned on the right-hand side

Phrases with *on*	Definition
on the internet	1 *checking news and information on the computer*
2 _____	for work reasons
on the right	3 _____
4 _____	travelling towards

2.4   Speaking and writing

Speaking   asking for and giving directions

1a Put the conversation in the right order 1–7.

___ Can you show us on the map?

___ Thanks.

___ That's right. It takes about ten minutes.

_1_ Please could you tell us how to get to the town hall?

___ Yes, here it is. You can't miss it.

___ Yes, go straight down here, cross the road at the lights and take the second left.

___ OK, so it's down here and second left after the lights?

b **2.4)))** Listen and check.

2 Choose the correct option to complete the sentences.

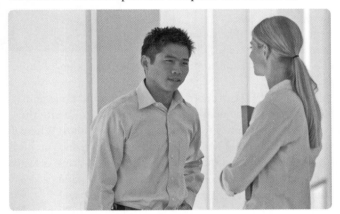

A Erm, I ¹ *'m looking* / *look* for the canteen.

B Yes, it's ² *on* / *in* the ground floor.

A Is it ³ *far* / *further*?

B No, not really. It's five minutes' ⁴ *walk* / *walking* from here.

A How do I get there?

B Go along the corridor, and ⁵ *take* / *turn* right at the end. Go down the ⁶ *stair* / *stairs* and you'll ⁷ *see* / *watch* the canteen in front of you.

A OK, so ⁸ *it's* / *there's* along here, right and down the stairs?

B That's right.

A Thanks.

3 Complete the conversation with the phrases in the box.

> a lot   I need to go   is this the right way   on the left
> that right   the first right   through the doors
> until you reach

A Excuse me, ¹ _is this the right way_ to the bathroom?

B Yes, keep going ² _____ the double doors. Go ³ _____ and take
⁴ _____.

A So ⁵ _____ through the double doors and turn right. Is ⁶ _____?

B Yes. It's the door ⁷ _____.

A Thanks ⁸ _____.

Writing   text messages

4 Rewrite the text messages using abbreviations.

> Hi! Where ¹ *are you*? Am waiting outside cinema. ² *See you* soon? ³ *Love Rachel.*

> ⁴ *Great!* ⁵ *Sorry* I'm late. Be there ⁶ *as soon as possible*. ⁷ *Please* could ⁸ *you* get tickets? ⁹ *Thanks!*

> Hi! Where ¹ _RU_ ? Am waiting outside cinema.
> ² _____ soon? ³ _____

> ⁴ _____! ⁵ _____ I'm late. Be there ⁶ _____. ⁷ _____ could
> ⁸ _____ get tickets? ⁹ _____!

I can …	Very well	Quite well	More practice
use phrases with *on*.	○	○	○
ask for and give directions.	○	○	○
write text messages.	○	○	○

2.5 Reading for pleasure

Pollution

1 Look at the photo. What kind of pollution does it show? Circle the correct answer 1, 2, 3 or 4.

1	air pollution	3	water pollution
2	noise pollution	4	land pollution

2 Read an extract from a short story called *Chemical Secret*.

3 Put the extract summary in the correct order 1–7.

____ John arrives in David Wilson's office.

____ David Wilson reads the report.

____ John says he's worried about the effects of the waste products.

____ Wilson says he doesn't like the conclusions in the report.

_1_ John does experiments to find out the effects of the waste products on rats and writes a report.

____ Wilson says he doesn't want to build new machines to clean up the waste products.

____ John gets very nervous and drinks water.

The story so far
John Duncan starts working in a factory. A few months later, he writes a report for his boss, David Wilson. Wilson calls John into his office to talk to him.

The report

'I've read your report,' Wilson began. Then he stopped. 'Not very good, is it?'

'What?' John stared at him in surprise.

Wilson smiled. 'No, no, don't worry – I don't mean the report is bad, of course not. You've worked very hard, and done your job well. What I mean is, I don't like the ideas at the end of the report.'

'What's wrong with them?'

'They're too expensive.' The two men stared at each other for a moment, and John felt cold and sick in his stomach. Wilson smiled, but it wasn't the kind of smile that John liked.

'Look, John,' he said. 'Your report says that we should build some new machines to clean up the waste products before they go into the river, right? And those machines will cost *two million pounds!* Where do you think we can find all that? Money doesn't grow on trees, you know!'

'No, of course not.' John's mouth was dry. He took a drink of water, and felt his hand shaking. 'But we're selling a lot of new paint. We're making millions of pounds every month from that, aren't we?'

'We're doing very well, yes,' said Wilson. 'But if we spend two million pounds to build these new machines, the paint will have to cost more, and we won't sell so much.'

'But – we've got to do it,' said John. 'These waste products are much more dangerous than I'd thought. Didn't you read that in my report? When I put the chemicals in rats' drinking water, some of the baby rats were born without eyes and ears. One didn't have any legs, and one had six.' He shivered. 'And some were born without legs when they drank only two parts per million. We can't put those chemicals in the river.'

Text extract from *Oxford Bookworms Factfiles: Chemical Secret*

4 Think about the events in the story.

Why do you think David Wilson doesn't want to spend money on the machines? Is it possible this kind of water pollution could happen in your country? Why/Why not?

Review: Units 1 and 2

Grammar

1 Complete the sentences with one word only.

1 She usually goes clubbing with some friends _who_ love dancing.
2 I do exercise _____ or twice a week.
3 What _____ of car do you drive?
4 He's driving _____ the moment so he can't talk on the phone.
5 My parents go on a trip _____ month.
6 How _____ do you have a family meal?

2 Choose the correct options to complete the advert.

Why not take a **trip**
down the **Nile?**

1 *Do you make* | *Are you making* plans now for your next summer holiday? If you **2** *want* | *are wanting* a trip with a difference, why not try a cruise down the River Nile? Our

boat **3** *leaves* | *is leaving* from Luxor every Monday morning and we **4** *don't arrive* | *aren't arriving* at our first stop until the next day. The trip **5** *lasts* | *is lasting* for seven nights and right now we **6** *offer* | *are offering* a special price. Just think what the guests **7** *do* | *are doing* right now! If you **8** *look* | *are looking* for a little adventure in your life, a Nile cruise is the trip for you. You're sure to have a lot of fun!

Vocabulary

3 Match definitions 1–8 to words and phrases in the box.

> dishwasher   do aerobics   do housework
> go out for a meal   have a lie-in   lively   stall   ~~towel~~

1 a thing you use to dry yourself _____ _towel_
2 get up late _____
3 a shop with an open front _____
4 do exercise to music _____
5 a machine that cleans plates, glasses, etc. _____
6 very exciting _____
7 clean the flat _____
8 have dinner in a restaurant _____

4 Complete the words in the text.

One of the largest cities in the world is Shanghai in China. The city is on the River Yangtze on the east coast and it's absolutely **1** h_uge_ – more than 23 million people live there. Houses are expensive because the city is so **2** cr_____, and most people live in very small flats. There isn't much room inside, so families don't often **3** st_____ in when they have free time. In the evenings, they go and sit outside: the adults on chairs and the children on a **4** r_____. Here they play **5** ch_____ together, tell stories or just **6** ch_____ with their friends. In the summer, it's too hot to go to bed so nobody has an **7** e_____ night.

5 Match words from A to words from B to form phrases. Then complete the sentences with the phrases.

A have   ~~on~~   on   on   make   take

B a dream   ~~holiday~~   a photograph   a promise
public transport   time

1 My neighbours aren't at home. They're _on holiday_.
2 I can't get to work _____. I have to take my car.
3 I often _____ about the house where I lived as a child.
4 When you get married you have to _____ to look after your partner.
5 You're always late. You're never _____.
6 We can't show you our hotel because we didn't _____ of it.

Speaking

6 Complete the conversations with the phrases in the box.

> Go straight down   I'm really   ~~I prefer~~   it's five minutes' walk

1 **A** What's your favourite season – summer or winter?
   B _I prefer_ summer to winter.
2 **A** Please could you tell me how to get to the sports centre?
   B Sure. _____ the road and turn left.
3 **A** Is it far to the park?
   B No, _____ from here.
4 **A** Which sport do you like best?
   B _____ into basketball.

Going up, going down

3.1 The man who fell to Earth

Vocabulary movement

1 Match definitions 1–9 to verbs in the box.

| climb dive drop ~~fall~~ jump land lift rise take off |

1 drop down towards the ground — *fall*
2 move upwards ___
3 come down from the air ___
4 leave the ground and start flying ___
5 move higher using your hands and feet ___
6 let something fall ___
7 move something up to a higher position ___
8 jump into the water with your arms and head first ___
9 move quickly into the air by pushing yourself up with your legs and feet ___

2 Choose the correct option to complete the sentences.

1 The wall wasn't very high, so my brother jumped *along /* (*over*)/ *towards* it.
2 Walk *backwards / forward / towards* the main square and the restaurant is on the left.
3 We all got *out of / over / through* the car when we arrived.
4 I went *along / into / round and round* the room and sat down opposite the interviewer.
5 It's quicker to go *forward / out of / through* the park, if it's open.
6 They couldn't turn the car around, so they had to drive *backwards / forwards / towards* down the track.
7 She can't decide what to do. She keeps going *into / round and round / out of* in circles.
8 They went for a pleasant walk *along / into / through* the path by the river.

3 Complete the information sheet with the prepositions in the box.

| along backwards forward ~~into~~ out of over through towards |

HOW TO STAY SAFE IN THE COUNTRY: BULLS

In general, try to keep away from bulls if you can. If you have to go ¹ _into_ a field where there is a bull, you need to be careful. Stay ² _____ the side of the field by the wall and don't try to run ³ _____ the middle. If the bull is looking at you, stop walking and don't move ⁴ _____ until it looks away again. If it starts making a noise and touching the ground with its foot, you need to get ⁵ _____ the field as soon as possible. Slowly walk ⁶ _____, and then climb ⁷ _____ the nearest wall. Then, if the bull comes ⁸ _____ you, you will already be safe.

Grammar   past simple

→ **STUDY TIP** There is a list of irregular verbs on p.166 of your Student's Book. Study the infinitive and past simple of five verbs every day so you can remember them easily. This will make it easier for you to use the past simple correctly.

4   Write sentences in the past simple using the words in brackets.

1   The plane from Madrid lands at 22.40. (night)
    The plane from Madrid landed at 22.40 last night.

2   The sun rises every morning. (two hours)
    _____

3   Do you go on holiday every year? (the summer)
    _____

4   We have a family meal every weekend. (day before yesterday)
    _____

5   I don't climb trees. (I was young)
    _____

6   My friends go clubbing. (three days)
    _____

7   Do you spend time with relatives? (other day)
    _____

8   We don't do housework during the week. (Tuesday)
    _____

PRONUNCIATION   irregular past verbs

5a   <u>Underline</u> the regular past simple form which has an extra syllable when you say the words.

1 dived	dropped	jumped	<u>landed</u>
2 booked	climbed	lifted	walked
3 arrived	travelled	turned	wanted
4 asked	looked	waited	worked
5 called	painted	played	listened
6 danced	helped	started	watched

b   **3.1** ⟩⟩ Listen and check.

c   **3.1** ⟩⟩ Listen again. Pause the CD and repeat after each word.

6   Complete the article with the correct past simple form of the verbs in brackets.

The first man in space

On 12th April 1961, Yuri Gagarin ¹ _became_ (become) the first man to travel into outer space. At 6.07 a.m. he ² _____ (take off) in his spacecraft, Vostok 1, and then he ³ _____ (fly) once around the Earth. Nearly two hours later, he ⁴ _____ (parachute) down towards the ground, but he ⁵ _____ (not land) in the right place. He ⁶ _____ (finish) his trip in a field 280 km away. A farmer and his daughter ⁷ _____ (see) him land, and at first they ⁸ _____ (be) very frightened. Gagarin was a hero when he ⁹ _____ (return) to Earth, but he ¹⁰ _____ (not retire) from work. Instead, he ¹¹ _____ (travel) around the world telling his story. After that, he ¹² _____ (work) for the Russian Air Force and he ¹³ _____ (help) to test new planes. Unfortunately, one of Gagarin's planes ¹⁴ _____ (crash) on 27th March 1968 and he ¹⁵ _____ (die) in the accident at the age of 34.

I can …	Very well	Quite well	More practice
describe movement.	○	○	○
talk about the past (1).	○	○	○

3.2   Going up … One man's lift nightmare

Vocabulary adjectives for describing feelings

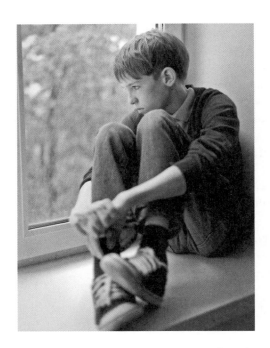

1a Complete the sentences with words in the box.

> angry anxious calm confused disappointed
> embarrassed ~~excited~~ exhausted guilty lonely
> nervous pleased scared stressed

1 We're _excited_ because we're going on holiday tomorrow.
2 My mother was _____ because we were late for dinner.
3 I'm _____ because I don't remember your name.
4 He felt _____ because he made his little sister cry.
5 They're _____ because they've got an exam tomorrow.
6 My cousin is _____ because he failed his driving test again.
7 My sister is _____ because she can't understand the instructions.
8 I feel _____ because I did yoga this morning.
9 She's _____ because she hasn't got any friends.
10 He feels _____ because it's late and his daughter isn't home.
11 I'm _____ because my job interview went well.

PRONUNCIATION adjective word stress (1)

b <u>Underline</u> the syllable we stress in the adjectives in exercise **1a**. Then complete the table.

One syllable	Two syllables	Three syllables	Four syllables
_____	_angry_	_____	_____
_____	_____	_____	
_____	_____		
_____	_____		
	_____		
	_____		

c 3.2))) Listen and check.

d 3.2))) Listen again. Pause the CD and repeat after each word.

2a Use the words in exercise **1a** to complete the puzzle.

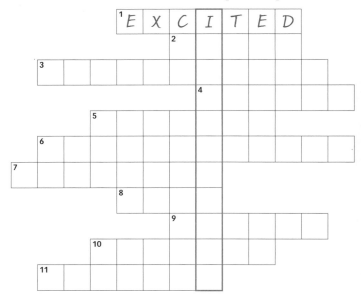

b What is the missing feeling?

Grammar   past simple and past continuous

3   Complete the sentences with the past continuous form of the verb in brackets.

1   It _was raining_ (rain) when we left the house.
2   The children _____ (sleep) when we got home.
3   My partner didn't call because his mobile phone _____ (not work).
4   What _____ you _____ (talk) about when I came in?
5   Who _____ (drive) when the accident happened?
6   You _____ (not watch) the TV so I turned it off.
7   I _____ (live) in Paris when I met my husband.
8   We _____ (dance) when the lights went out.

4   Write sentences with *when*. Use the past simple and the past continuous.

1   I / drop a glass / I / do the washing up
    I dropped a glass when I was doing the washing up.
2   we / study in the library / the fire / start
    _____
3   my partner / break his leg / he / play football
    _____
4   a thief / take my bag / I / sit in the park
    _____
5   you / come out of the supermarket / I / see you
    _____
6   my friends / wait outside the cinema / I / arrive
    _____

5   Complete the article with the past simple or past continuous form of the verb in brackets.

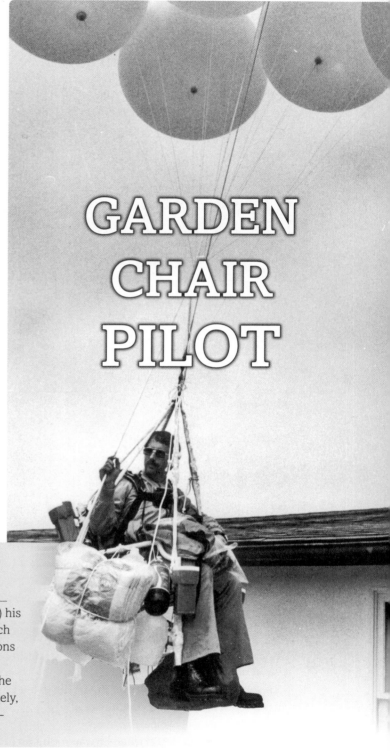

GARDEN CHAIR PILOT

When Larry Walters was a teenager, he [1] _saw_ (see) some balloons while he [2] _____ (do) the shopping one day. He [3] _____ (think) about using them to fly, but he [4] _____ (not try) the idea until twenty years later. He [5] _____ (ask) his girlfriend and a friend to tie 45 balloons to a garden chair which he [6] _____ (sit) in. Then, they [7] _____ (fill) the balloons with helium. Immediately, Larry [8] _____ (rise) to a height of 3,600 m and he was very frightened. Then he noticed that the chair [9] _____ (go) towards Los Angeles Airport. Fortunately, he [10] _____ (come) down three-quarters of an hour later – before he reached the airport.

I can ...	Very well	Quite well	More practice
talk about feelings.	○	○	○
talk about the past (2).	○	○	○

3.3 Vocabulary development

Vocabulary   adverbs of manner

1 Rewrite the sentences with verb + adverb.

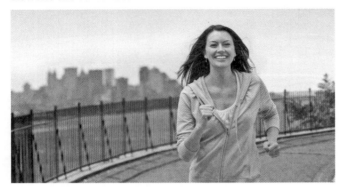

1 They're bad tennis players.
   They play tennis badly.

2 He's a slow reader.
   _____

3 We're healthy eaters.
   _____

4 My mother is a fast walker.
   _____

5 I'm a careful driver.
   _____

6 You're a good cook.
   _____

7 My partner is a hard worker.
   _____

8 My brother is a smart dresser.
   _____

2 Complete the sentences with the adverb form of the adjectives in the box.

| beautiful   easy   fluent   polite   quick   quiet   ~~regular~~ |

1 My sister goes on business _regularly_. She's hardly ever at home.
2 Can you talk _____ please? I'm trying to read.
3 I used my GPS, so I found your house _____.
4 That girl has a lovely voice. She sings _____.
5 My partner lived in Berlin when he was young, so he speaks German _____.
6 Walk _____! We're going to be late!
7 She smiled _____ when I said hello, but I don't think she recognized me.

Vocabulary review

3 Complete the table with the headings in the box.

| going down   going up |

1 _____	2 _____
climb	dive
jump	drop
lift	fall
rise	jump
take off	land

4 Complete the table with the adjectives in the box.

| anxious   embarrassed   ~~excited~~   lonely   pleased   scared |

Positive feelings	Negative feelings
calm	angry
1 _excited_	2 _____
in a good mood	confused
3 _____	disappointed
	4 _____
	exhausted
	guilty
	5 _____
	nervous
	6 _____
	stressed

5 Complete the table below.

Adjective	Adverb
angry	1 _angrily_
2 _____	nicely
easy	3 _____
4 _____	fast
polite	5 _____

3.4   Speaking and writing

Speaking telling and responding to a story

1a Complete the conversations with the words and phrases in the box.

> a funny thing happened   anyway   I was so angry
> it was all OK in the end   oh no   what happened
> ~~we had a bad experience~~   we were so pleased!
> you're joking

Conversation 1

A ¹ <u>*We had a bad experience*</u>   when we were on holiday a few years ago. We hired a car and went exploring on the coast.

B Where were you?

A In the Canary Islands – in Fuerteventura, to be exact. So, ² _____,
we were in this hired car and we decided to leave the main road. We were driving in some sand when, suddenly, the car got stuck.

B ³ _____!

A That's what I thought. ⁴ _____ with my husband – he went right when I said left, and suddenly, we were lost and stuck.

B So, what did you do?

A We walked about five kilometres to the nearest road, and then we got a taxi back to our hotel, where we called for help. ⁵ _____, but it cost us €250 to get the car out of the sand!

Conversation 2

A ⁶ _____ last weekend when we went for a walk. We parked our car in a pretty little village and walked over the mountains to the next village. We were hoping to get a bus back to our car.

B So, ⁷ _____?

A We asked in a café about the buses, but there weren't any.

B ⁸ _____!

A No, it's true. The café was full, so we left and started looking for a place to have lunch. We were walking along the road when a woman stopped her car and told us to get in.

B Why did she do that?

A She heard us ask about the buses in the café, so she knew where we wanted to go. You see, she was working in the village where our car was, and so she took us there on the way to work. ⁹ _____!

b 3.3))) Listen and check.

Writing email (1): describing an event

2 Choose the correct options to complete the email.

> ☒
>
> Hi John,
>
> It was great to hear from you. Yes, thanks, I had a great time visiting my family. The best day was when we all went for a walk together. We started walking at midday and ¹ *a short time later / finally / while*, something really funny happened. We were walking along by the side of a river, ² *after a few minutes / then / when* my brother decided to try and jump across it. ³ *Suddenly / To begin with / While*, we saw him run towards the river, so we all stopped to watch him. Unfortunately, the river was wider than he thought and he landed right in the middle. ⁴ *At first / But after / Half an hour later*, we didn't say anything, ⁵ *at last / but then / next* my brother started laughing. That made the rest of us laugh, too. ⁶ *At first / When / In the end*, my sister went to help him get out of the river. As you can imagine, he was very wet!
>
> Anyway, I'll call you soon to see when I can show you the photos.
>
> Love, Jane

I can …	Very well	Quite well	More practice
understand and use adverbs of manner.	○	○	○
tell and respond to a story.	○	○	○
write an informal email describing an event.	○	○	○

Changes and challenges

4.1 Changing directions

Vocabulary life stages and events

1 Complete the sentences with the life stages in the box.

> about thirty-five   a child   elderly   in (her) early twenties
> in (her) late twenties   ~~in (my) mid-twenties~~   in (her) sixties
> middle-aged   a teenager

1 I'm 25 on my next birthday. I'm _in my mid-twenties_.
2 My mum is 50. She's _____.
3 My sister is 21. She's _____.
4 My grandmother is 75. She's _____.
5 My sister-in-law is 28. She's _____.
6 My aunt is 63. She's _____.
7 My cousin is in her mid-thirties. She's _____.
8 My niece is eight. She's _____.
9 My other niece is fifteen. She's _____.

2 Match verbs 1–8 to phrases a–h to make life events.

1 change   a to swim
2 get   b time abroad
3 learn   c home
4 leave   d career
5 live   e a job
6 move   f house
7 pass   g with a partner
8 spend   h your driving test

3 Complete the phrases with the words in the box.

> have   go to   choose   get   leave   ~~start~~

1 _start_ your own business
2 _____ your career
3 _____ university
4 _____ a baby
5 _____ married
6 _____ home

4 Complete the article about Bill Gates with the correct past simple form of the verbs in the box.

> decide   get   go   have   leave   retire   start   ~~take up~~

BILL GATES:

Success story

Born in 1955, Bill Gates ¹ _took up_ computing when he was at high school. But when he ² _____ school, he ³ _____ to follow the same career as his father and he ⁴ _____ to university to study Law. Later, however, he changed to maths and computer science instead. In 1975, while he was still at university, he started writing computer software for a company called MITS. In 1977, he ⁵ _____ his own company, Microsoft, and ten years later, he became the youngest billionaire ever. The same year, he met his future wife, Melinda, and in 1994, they ⁶ _____ married. The couple ⁷ _____ their first child in 1996 and another two children in 1999 and 2002. Today, Bill Gates is one of the richest men in the world, although he ⁸ _____ from his normal job at Microsoft in 2008.

Grammar verbs with -ing and to

5 Put the words in the right order to make questions.

1 learn did when drive you to
   When did you learn to drive?

2 did to you what wear decide
   _____

3 win you did to who want
   _____

4 to much you plan did spend how
   _____

5 would go like where to you
   _____

6 did stop why to you need
   _____

PRONUNCIATION weak form of *to*

6a 4.1))) Listen and check your answers to exercise **5**. Pay attention to the weak /tə/ pronunciation of *to*.

b 4.1))) Listen again. Pause the CD and repeat after each word.

---

7 Choose the correct option to complete the sentences.

1 I learned *to play* / *playing* the piano when I was a child.
2 Do you like *to live* / *living* in the country?
3 I hope *to retire* / *retiring* before I'm 65.
4 My brother stopped *to play* / *playing* basketball when he went to university.
5 I can't stand *to go* / *going* to the dentist's.
6 When did you decide *to move* / *moving* house?
7 My girlfriend enjoys *to do* / *doing* aerobics.
8 If it keeps *to rain* / *raining*, we'll go home.

→ **STUDY TIP** Have one page for verbs with *-ing* and another page for verbs with *to* in your notebook. Make a note of new verbs as you come across them. This will make it easier for you to remember how to use the verbs.

---

8 Complete the article with the correct form of the verbs in the box.

apply ask be do get up go leave look for think ~~work~~

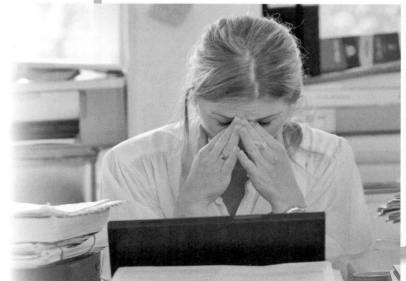

HOME | ABOUT | **NEWS** | BLOG

The **right** way to **change** your job

What can you do if you can't stand ¹ *working* in the job that you're in and you'd like ² _____ something different? Below are some tips to help you if you're in this situation.

First of all, you need ³ _____ about what you like and don't like about your current job. This will help you decide the kind of job you want ⁴ _____ for.

If you decide ⁵ _____ a new job, spend some time updating your CV. Then send your new one to all your contacts. Learn ⁶ _____ patient, because changing your job can take a long time!

Even if you hate ⁷ _____ for work every morning, it's important to keep ⁸ _____ to the office until you have a new job.

When you get a job offer, plan ⁹ _____ your current job after you've had a holiday – imagine ¹⁰ _____ your new boss for two weeks off on your first day!

I can ...	Very well	Quite well	More practice
talk about life stages and events.	○	○	○
use verbs with *-ing* or *to*.	○	○	○

4.2 Living without the internet

Vocabulary internet activities

1   Replace the words in **bold** with the verbs and phrases in the box.

> blog   chat online   do research   ~~go online~~   log on   shop online
> tweet   use social media

1   Do you **use the internet** every day? _go online_
2   Do you ever **look for information** online? _____
3   Do any of your friends **regularly update their personal website**?
    _____
4   How often do you **talk to your friends on your computer or smartphone**? _____
5   Do you ever **post comments on the social networking site Twitter**?
    _____
6   Do you ever **buy things on the internet**? _____
7   Which is the first website you **connect** to every day? _____
8   How often do you **go on Facebook or Twitter**? _____

2a   Match verbs in box A to words in box B to make phrases. Then complete the sentences with the phrases.

> **A**   deal   do   download   post   read   share   ~~text~~   update

> **B**   ~~friends~~   music   online banking   personal information on a website
> photos   the news   with emails   your Facebook page

1   **A**   What do you do when you're feeling lonely?
    B   I _text friends_ . They always make me feel better.
2   **A**   What's the first thing you do on Monday mornings?
    B   I _____. I usually have hundreds to answer.
3   **A**   Do you ever buy a newspaper?
    B   No, I _____ on the internet.
4   **A**   Where do you pay your electricity bill?
    B   On the internet. I _____ so I don't have to leave my house.
5   **A**   How often do you use social media?
    B   A lot. But you don't need to _____ every day – you can add photos and comments when you like.
6   **A**   How did you listen to that song?
    B   On my mobile phone. I often _____ from the internet.
7   **A**   Have you got a digital camera?
    B   No, I use my phone because it's easier to _____ with my friends.
8   **A**   Are you worried about internet security?
    B   Not really. I never _____.

b   **4.2))** Now listen and check.

3   Complete the article with eight of the verbs in exercises **1** and **2a**.

The changing face of social media

If you **¹** _use_ social media, you'll know that Facebook and Twitter are two of the most popular sites. Users **²**_____ online several times a day to **³**_____ to their account and check what's new. You can **⁴**_____ photos and **⁵**_____ videos on both sites but, in fact, they are quite different. Most people use Twitter to **⁶**_____ the news or follow celebrities who **⁷**_____ messages about what they're doing. Of course, it's easier to **⁸**_____ online on Facebook, because you can write as many words as you like. These sites are popular now, but the internet is always changing, so perhaps in the future we will use different ones.

| **Oxford 3000™**

Grammar   *going to* and present continuous for the future

4   Write sentences with *going to* for photos 1–6.

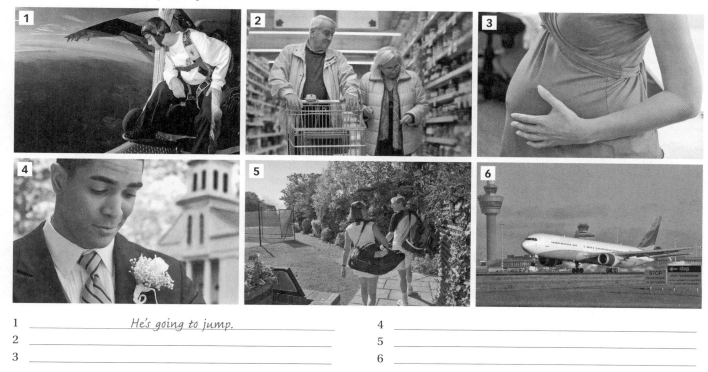

1 _____ *He's going to jump.* _____   4 _____
2 _____   5 _____
3 _____   6 _____

5   Choose the more likely option, *be going to* or present continuous, to complete the conversations.

1   **A** Why are you turning the computer on?
    B Because I'm *checking /* ⟨*going to check*⟩ my emails.
2   **A** Your boyfriend's Facebook page still says he's single.
    B I know. He's *updating / going to update* it at the weekend.
3   **A** Would you like to have dinner with us on Sunday?
    B Sorry, we can't. My in-laws *are coming / are going to come* round.
4   **A** Where's your girlfriend going this evening?
    B She's *having / going to have* a coffee with a friend.
5   **A** Why did they tell us to sit down?
    B Because the plane *is landing / is going to land*.
6   **A** Let's go to the cinema tonight.
    B I can't. I'm *working / going to work* late.

6   Complete the conversation with the most suitable form of the verb in brackets, *be going to* or present continuous.

A It's your birthday soon, isn't it?
B Yes, it's on 11th March. [1] _*I'm going to be*_ (I/be) 40.
A 40! [2] _____ (you/have) a party on the Big Day?
B No, I've got other plans. [3] _____ (I/take) a few days off with my wife.
A How exciting! Tell me all about it.
B [4] _____ (we/visit) Paris that weekend.
   [5] _____ (I/not work) on the Friday, so
   [6] _____ (we/fly) on Friday morning.
   Then [7] _____ (we/come) back on Sunday evening.
A What [8] _____ (you/do) in Paris?
B [9] _____ (we/go up) the Eiffel Tower, obviously. And [10] _____ (we/see) a show at the Moulin Rouge, too – I've already got the tickets.
A Well, I hope you have a great time.
B Thanks.

I can …	Very well	Quite well	More practice
talk about using the internet.	○	○	○
talk about plans and arrangements.	○	○	○

4.3 Vocabulary development

Vocabulary *get*

1 Complete the sentences with *get* and the words in the box.

> bored   cold   home   a job   ~~married~~   a phone call
> some pizzas   some shoes

1 They lived together for ten years before they decided to *get married* .
2 I've got a dress for my sister's wedding, but I need to _____.
3 How do you feel when you _____ in the middle of the night?
4 I go to work at 7.30 every morning, and I don't _____ until 8 p.m.
5 Is your brother going to university, or is he going to _____?
6 I don't feel like cooking. Can you _____ on the way home from work?
7 I _____ when I go on long journeys.
8 Winter starts next month, so it's going to _____.

2 Respond to the sentences with *get* and the words in the box.

> any presents   home earlier   a job   ~~a new one~~
> ready   a taxi

1 **A** My car isn't working.
   B Why don't *you get a new one?*
2 **A** My partner hasn't got any money.
   B Why doesn't he _____
3 **A** We're going clubbing tonight.
   B Why don't you _____
4 **A** I had a horrible birthday.
   B Why didn't you _____
5 **A** It's late, and there aren't any buses.
   B Why don't we _____
6 **A** She never has time to have dinner.
   B Why doesn't she _____

Vocabulary review

3a Complete the phrases with the words in the box.

> ~~about~~   abroad   -aged   career   go to   have   in   married
> partner   sixties

1 *about* thirty-five
2 in your _____
3 change _____
4 get _____
5 _____ your early twenties
6 _____ university
7 _____ a baby
8 middle _____
9 live with a _____
10 spend time _____

b Which are life stages and which are life events in exercise **3a**?

4 Match verbs 1–11 to words and phrases a–k to form internet activities.

1 blog
2 go/chat/shop
3 deal with
4 do
5 download
6 log
7 post
8 read/listen
9 share
10 update
11 use

a (sth) on a website
b social media
c to the news
d and tweet
e research/online banking
f pictures
g online
h your Facebook page
i on/out
j emails
k films/music/apps

5 Complete the mind map with the verbs in the box to match the meaning of *get*.

> buy   become   receive

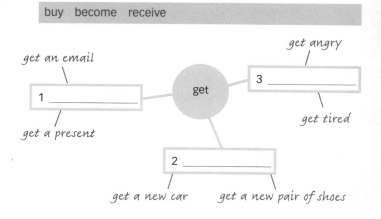

get an email
get a present
get a new car   get a new pair of shoes
get angry
get tired
1 _____
get
3 _____
2 _____

4.4 Speaking and writing

inviting & making arrangements

1a Put the conversation in the correct order 1–8.

___ Sure. Is two o'clock OK for you?

___ I'm working on Saturday, but I'm free on Sunday.

___ Yeah, I'd love to.

_1_ Are you doing anything at the weekend?

___ Shall we meet outside the museum when it opens?

___ Two o'clock is perfect. See you there.

___ I'm afraid I can't go that early, because I'm playing tennis. Could we meet in the afternoon instead?

___ Do you fancy going to the Renoir exhibition at the Prado?

PRONUNCIATION inviting phrases

b **4.3**)) Listen and check your answers.

c **4.3**)) Listen again. Pause the CD and repeat after each word.

2 Complete the conversation with the phrases in the box.

> I'd like   ~~are you free~~   be great   how about   would you like
> I can't make it   any good   sounds perfect   we could try

A ¹ _Are you free_ next weekend?

B It depends. Why?

A It's my birthday on Friday and I'm having a party.
²_____ to come?

B I'm really sorry, but ³_____ on Friday because I'm going to the theatre with some friends. ⁴_____ having lunch together instead?

A That'd ⁵_____!

B ⁶_____ the new Japanese restaurant on the high street.

A Yes, ⁷_____ that. Is one o'clock ⁸_____ for you?

B ⁹_____. See you on Friday.

email (2): making arrangements

3 Look at the phrases below and choose the more informal ones. Then complete the email with the informal phrases.

- All the best / Love
- could we go out / how about going out
- Dear Suzanne / Hi there!
- How are you doing? / I hope you are well
- I'd love to / We could
- I hope to hear from you soon / Speak soon
- I'm afraid / I'm really sorry but
- Is that OK for you? / Please let me know if that's OK

> ⊠   Sent: Friday 10.37
>
> ¹ _Hi there!_
>
> ²_____
>
> ³_____ I can't make it to your birthday party. I'm going on a trip with my girlfriend that weekend so I won't be around.
>
> Anyway, ⁴_____ for a meal next week instead? Shall we meet for dinner on Friday evening? ⁵_____ try the new Italian restaurant next to the cinema. ⁶_____
>
> Hope the party goes well.
>
> ⁷_____
>
> ⁸_____
>
> Rob

I can …	Very well	Quite well	More practice
understand and use *get*.	○	○	○
invite and make arrangements.	○	○	○
write an email to make arrangements.	○	○	○

4.5 Listening for pleasure

Ecological housing

1 Label the photo with the building materials in the box.

> bricks ~~concrete~~ glass metal
> plastic wood

2 **4.4**))) Listen to a radio programme about a company that makes special houses.

3 **4.4**))) Listen again and complete the summary with the words and numbers in the box.

> floor parts 150 ~~printer~~ 100 3,650 small waste

The WinSun Decoration Design Engineering Company makes special houses using a 3D ¹ *printer* . The machine is ² _____ metres long and ten metres wide. It prints the houses in ³ _____ that people can put together later. The material for the houses is made from recycled industrial ⁴ _____. The company is going to build ⁵ _____ new factories to do the recycling. The houses are quite ⁶ _____ and they only have one ⁷ _____. They cost around ⁸ € _____.

4 Think about the Chinese houses in the recording. Do you like the idea of houses like these? Why/Why not? Would they be popular in your country? Why/Why not?

Review: Units 3 and 4

Grammar

1 Choose the correct option to complete the sentences.

1 My sister enjoys *going* / *to go* to concerts.
2 I hope *retiring* / *to retire* before I'm 67.
3 We plan *starting* / *to start* our own business next year.
4 Can you imagine *changing* / *to change* your career?
5 My parents want *moving* / *to move* house.
6 They stopped *playing* / *to play* football when they left school.
7 Would you like *coming* / *to come* for dinner on Saturday evening?
8 My son keeps *failing* / *to fail* his exams.

2 Complete the conversation with the correct form of *be going to* and the words in brackets.

A What **1** *are your parents going to do* (your parents/do) when they retire?
B Well, first **2**_____ (they/relax). But then, they have some plans. **3**_____ (they/not stay) at home all day.
A What **4**_____ (your dad/do)?
B **5**_____ (he/learn) Spanish. And **6**_____ (my mum/take up) a new hobby. She says she'd like to do yoga.

3 Complete the article with the past simple or past continuous form of the verbs in brackets.

Escape artist

Erik Weisz is better known as the escape artist Harry Houdini. He was born in Budapest, Hungary, but his family **1** *moved* (move) to the USA when he was only a child. He was 17 when his magic career began, but he **2**_____ (not make) a lot of money at first. When he was 19, he met his wife while he **3**_____ (do) a show, and from then on the two **4**_____ (appear) together. The Houdinis **5**_____ (become) famous because of Harry's escape acts, which he did in front of a crowd. People usually felt very nervous while they **6**_____ (watch) him. Houdini always said that he **7**_____ (not feel) pain, so one day a student asked if he could test him. The man hit him in the stomach, but Houdini **8**_____ (lie) in bed at the time, so he wasn't in a good position. He died a few days later at the age of 52.

Vocabulary

4 Complete the sentences with a suitable word.

1 Her parents were very pl*eased* when she and her boyfriend got engaged.
2 It was hot so we couldn't wait to d_____ into the swimming pool.
3 I felt l_____ when I first moved house.
4 Please don't dr_____ that mirror. It'll break.
5 He felt g_____ when he made his little sister cry.
6 I'll pick you up from the airport. What time do you l_____?

5 Complete the text with the verbs in the box.

deal with   do   get   go   ~~leave~~   log on   retire   text

Every year, the number of internet users rises. The most frequent users are teenagers between the ages of 16 and 18, but once they **1** *leave* school, these young adults don't **2**_____ online as often. The internet is also popular with the elderly. Once people **3**_____, they have more time to **4**_____ to a computer and **5**_____ emails, for example. Teenagers use the internet on their mobile phones to **6**_____ friends on instant messaging services. Today more people **7**_____ online banking than before. People are also using the internet to try and **8**_____ a job.

Speaking

6 Complete the conversation with the phrases in the box.

~~are you free~~   do you fancy   how about   I'd love to
I had a bad experience   shall we   what happened
you're joking

A Abigail, **1** *are you free* on Saturday night?
B Yes, I think so. Why?
A **2**_____ going out for a meal?
B Yeah, **3**_____. Where are you thinking of going?
A **4**_____ trying that fish restaurant on the high street?
B Oh no! **5**_____ the last time I went there.
A Really? **6**_____?
B I was so ill the next day that I had to go to hospital.
A **7**_____! Well, **8**_____ go to an Indian restaurant instead?

5 Stuff and things

5.1 Your world in objects

Vocabulary adjectives for describing objects

1 Circle the word or phrase that is different.
  1 dark blue   metal   pale grey
  2 large   tiny   useful
  3 comfortable   heavy   light
  4 leather   plastic   thin
  5 gold   personal   ordinary
  6 antique   brand new   special

2 Match definitions 1–8 to words in the box.

> amazing gold leather light ordinary special useful valuable

  1 made from an expensive metal   _gold_
  2 not weighing much   _____
  3 difficult to believe   _____
  4 made from the skin of animals   _____
  5 important for some reason   _____
  6 helpful and practical   _____
  7 costing a lot of money   _____
  8 very normal   _____

3 Complete the article with the words in the box.

> amazing antique brand new comfortable heavy large thin tiny

Televisions:

past and present

It's ¹ _amazing_ how much televisions have changed over the years. Early televisions were very ² _____ and they needed at least two people to carry them. It was difficult to see the image on an ³ _____ television, because the screen was ⁴ _____. Today, ⁵ _____ televisions are a completely different shape. They are very ⁶ _____, which makes them easier to carry, and they have a ⁷ _____ screen, which is easy to see. And watching TV is much more ⁸ _____ these days, because you don't have to get up from the sofa every time you want to change the channel!

PRONUNCIATION adjective word stress (2)

4a Underline the syllable we stress in the words. Which word has the stress on the second syllable?
  1 useful   5 special
  2 heavy   6 antique
  3 leather   7 plastic
  4 metal   8 tiny

b **5.1**))) Listen and check.

c **5.1**))) Listen again. Pause the CD and repeat after each word.

Grammar   articles

5   Choose the correct option *a/an*, *the* or (✗) (= nothing) to complete the sentences.

1   It's my mother's birthday so I need to buy ⓐ/ *the* / (✗) present.

2   Your coat is hanging in *a* / *the* / (✗) wardrobe.

3   I've forgotten *a* / *the* / (✗) name of that film we saw last night.

4   I've never liked *a* / *the* / (✗) big dogs, especially if they're barking.

5   Yesterday was *an* / *the* / (✗) ordinary day – we didn't do anything special.

6   *A* / *The* / (✗) ring my partner gave me is very valuable.

7   We never eat *a* / *the* / (✗) fast food because it isn't very healthy.

8   Our dishwasher is broken so we need to buy *a* / *the* / (✗) new one.

6   Read the article. Tick (✓) the correct articles and put a cross (✗) if the article is wrong. Correct the incorrect articles.

1	✓	7	
2	✗ *the planets*	8	
3		9	
4		10	
5		11	
6		12	

7   Complete the conversations with *a/an*, *the* or (✗) (= nothing).

1   **A**   Where is __the__ milk?
     B   I put it back in _____ fridge.

2   **A**   Do you want to have _____ shower?
     B   Yes, please. Can I have _____ towel?

3   **A**   Have you got _____ car?
     B   Yes, but I prefer using _____ public transport.

4   **A**   I've just read _____ great book. I cried at the end.
     B   Really? I don't like _____ books with sad endings.

5   **A**   Where can I find information about _____ cheap flights?
     B   On _____ internet.

6   **A**   Do your parents live in _____ house where you were born?
     B   No, they moved to _____ countryside when they retired.

Time capsules in space

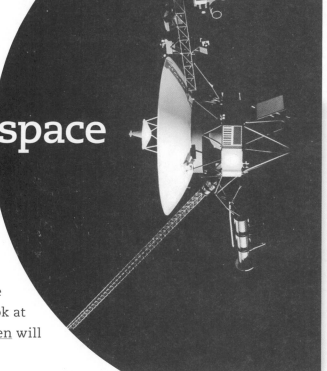

In 1977, NASA sent *Voyager* 1 and *Voyager* 2 into [1]space to study [2]planets Jupiter and Saturn. Each Voyager is carrying [3]time capsule with [4]pictures that show [5]the life on Earth. [6]The capsules also contain [7]the music and different sounds, such as [8]the birds singing. Each capsule is [9]a present for the person who finds it. In the future, someone may look at [10]pictures and listen to [11]music. Or perhaps [12]an alien will find one. Who knows?

I can ...	Very well	Quite well	More practice
describe objects.	◯	◯	◯
use articles.	◯	◯	◯

5.2 It's all about the money

Vocabulary money

1a 5.2))) Listen and write six words connected to money.

1 _bag_____ _c_   4 _____ ___
2 _____ ___   5 _____ ___
3 _____ ___   6 _____ ___

b 5.2))) Listen again and repeat the words.

c Match photos a–f to words 1–6 in exercise **1a**.

a

b

c

d

e

f

2 Complete the words in the sentences.

1 Do you usually pay for your shopping in c_ash_ or by credit card?
2 Do you have any ch_____ in your pocket right now?
3 How old were you when you opened your first b_____ a_____?
4 Have you ever been i_____ d_____ to a member of your family?
5 Do you know the exact a_____ of money in your purse or wallet?
6 Where do you check your b_____ – at the bank or on the internet?
7 Do you own your house or flat or do you pay r_____?

3 Complete the text with the correct form of the verbs in the box.

| afford | borrow | lend | ~~owe~~ | pay for | save up | spend |

Borrowing from the bank

Most of us [1] _owe_ money to a bank at some time in our lives because we can't [2] _____ to buy a place to live without some help. Some people [3] _____ for the future when they are living with their parents, and others [4] _____ all their money on clothes and going out. But nearly everybody [5] _____ money from a bank to [6] _____ their first house. The problem is that when a bank [7] _____ you a lot of money, it can take many years to pay it back.

Grammar quantifiers

4 Choose the correct option to complete the sentences.

1 We took *any* / *some* great photos while we were on holiday.

2 My partner is very keen on reading. She's got *a lot of* / *too much* books.

3 There's too *much* / *many* sugar in my coffee. I can't drink it.

4 We live in a small village. There are only a *little* / *few* houses.

5 How *much* / *many* credit cards have you got?

6 The bill is right. There aren't *any* / *some* mistakes.

7 Do you do *many* / *much* exercise?

8 My brother has *enough* / *too many* money to buy a brand new car.

5 Complete the conversation with the quantifiers in the box.

> a few   a little   any   enough   lots of   many   much
> ~~some~~   too much

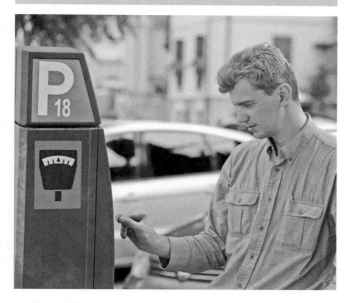

A Great! We managed to find a parking space.

B Yes, but now we need ¹ *some* money for the machine. Have you got ² _____ change?

A Yes, I think I've got ³ _____ coins in my purse, but not many. How ⁴ _____ money do we need?

B It depends how long we stay. Will 20 minutes give us ⁵ _____ time to speak to the manager?

A I'm not sure. There are usually ⁶ _____ people in the bank on Fridays and it can take a long time.

B OK, how about an hour?

A No, that's ⁷ _____ time. We don't have ⁸ _____ questions to ask. Let's put 40 minutes.

B Right. Come on, then. Let's go.

6 Complete the conversations with a quantifier from box A and a noun from box B.

> **A** ~~a few~~ a little any enough lots of some
> too many too much

> **B** biscuits ~~days~~ food friends petrol Portuguese
> shopping things

1 A How long were you away?
  B Only *a few days* . Just for the weekend.

2 A Why did you call a taxi?
  B I had _____ . I couldn't carry it all.

3 A Can you speak any foreign languages?
  B Yes, I speak English, Spanish and _____ .

4 A Are you going camping alone?
  B No, we're going with _____ . There will be six of us.

5 A Why aren't you hungry?
  B I've eaten _____ . I finished the packet and I don't feel well!

6 A What's your hometown like?
  B Very interesting. There are _____ to see and do.

7 A What's the matter with the car?
  B We've stopped. We haven't got _____ .

8 A Would you like a sandwich?
  B No, thanks. I've eaten _____ for one day.

I can ...	Very well	Quite well	More practice
talk about money.	○	○	○
talk about quantity.	○	○	○

5.3 Vocabulary development

Vocabulary suffixes

1 Complete the sentences with the correct form of the words in brackets.

1 My parents bought a new _digital_ camera for their holiday. (digit)
2 We haven't got any _____ for next weekend. (arrange)
3 I had a great time at the party. It was very _____. (enjoy)
4 Have you found a _____ for your house yet? (buy)
5 I never drive in the city centre. It's too _____. (stress)
6 It was a _____ day, the same as every other. (norm)
7 You have to pay extra to take sports _____ on a plane. (equip)
8 The match was a real _____. We lost 5-0. (disappoint)
9 We didn't sleep well because the beds weren't very _____. (comfort)
10 Can you give me some _____ about the exhibition, please? (inform)

2 Complete the text with the correct form of the words in brackets.

> If you have made the ¹ _decision_ (DECIDE) to throw away some of your ² _____ (POSSESS), then why not take them to a charity shop? These shops are ³ _____ (ESSENCE) for people in need, because your old things make money to help them. You can also find many ⁴ _____ (USE) things in the shops to buy. There are leather bags, children's toys and ⁵ _____ (BEAUTY) cards which you can send to friends and family on their birthdays. The clothes aren't usually very ⁶ _____ (FASHION), but you can sometimes find something ⁷ _____ (SUIT) for a special occasion. In some of the shops you can even find ⁸ _____ (COMPUTE)!

➔ **STUDY TIP** Some words are easier to remember than others. Write an example sentence for the words that you find particularly difficult and try to memorize the sentence. This will help you remember difficult words.

Vocabulary review

3 Complete the table with the headings in the box.

age ~~colour~~ material opinion size / shape weight

1 _colour_	dark blue pale grey
2 _____	amazing comfortable ordinary personal special useful
3 _____	heavy light
4 _____	gold leather metal plastic
5 _____	antique brand new
6 _____	large thin tiny

4 Complete the table with the words in the box.

afford ~~balance~~ cash lend note pay for rent save up

Money: nouns

amount   bag   ¹ _balance_   bank account   bill   ² _____   change   coin   credit card   ³ _____   purse   receipt   ⁴ _____   ticket   wallet

Money: verbs

⁵ _____   borrow   ⁶ _____   owe   ⁷ _____   ⁸ _____   spend … on

5 Complete the table with the correct form of the words in the box.

buy ~~disappoint~~ inform norm suit use

Noun suffixes

-ment: arrangement,   ¹ _disappointment_ ,   equipment

-ion: condition,   ² _____ ,   possession

-er: ³ _____ ,   computer,   scooter

Adjective suffixes

-ful: beautiful,   stressful,   ⁴ _____

-able: comfortable,   enjoyable,   fashionable,   ⁵ _____

-al: digital,   essential,   ⁶ _____

5.4   Speaking and writing

explaining words you don't know

1a   Put the conversation in the correct order 1–9.

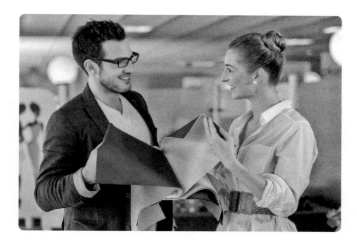

___   That's right. Do you know what I mean?

___   Well, can you describe it for me?

___   Oh, hello. Yes, I am, but I don't know the word in English.

___   Yes, it's a thing that you use to keep warm in the winter.

_1_   Good morning. Are you looking for anything in particular?

___   No, it looks like a carpet, but it's smaller.

___   Yes, I do. It's a rug. Come with me and I'll show you where they are.

___   Is it something you wear?

___   And do you put it on the floor?

b   **5.3**))) Listen and check.

2   Complete the conversation with the phrases in the box.

> Exactly! That's what I'm looking for.   ~~what's it called?~~
> You use it to dry yourself   I've forgotten the word in English.
> It's quite big, like a sheet.

A   Hi. Can I help you?

B   Yes, I'm looking for … ¹ _what's it called?_

A   Yes?

B   ² _____.

A   Well, what does it look like?

B   ³ _____.

A   Do you mean a duvet?

B   No, no. ⁴ _____ after you have a shower.

A   Oh! You mean a towel!

B   ⁵ _____.

A   Good. The towels are over there on the right.

B   Thank you very much.

A   You're welcome.

email (3): returning an online product

3   Complete the email with the phrases in the box.

> Could you please send   get a refund   I didn't receive
> I'm afraid I'm not happy   I'd like to return   Yours sincerely
> ~~recently ordered~~   they are completely different

Dear Sir/Madam,

Re: order number 492JM

¹ I _recently ordered_ some headphones from your online store. I received them this morning, but ² _____ with them because they're damaged. Also, ³ _____ from the headphones in the photo on the website. Those were purple and they came with a purple bag. ⁴ _____ the bag.

As a result, ⁵ _____ the headphones.

⁶ _____ me the headphones that are in the photo on the website? If this is not possible, I would like to ⁷ _____.

⁸ _____

Yasmin Husseini

I can …	Very well	Quite well	More practice
understand and use suffixes.	○	○	○
explain words I don't know.	○	○	○
write an email to return an online product.	○	○	○

6.1 The quiet revolution

Vocabulary adjectives for describing character

1 Complete the puzzle to discover the hidden adjective.

¹ S O C I A B L E

1 not shy about speaking with people
2 very intelligent
3 not talking much
4 not wanting to work
5 not putting things in the right place
6 very sure about what you are doing
7 not stupid
8 not telling lies

2 Choose the correct option to complete the sentences.
1 You're really *clever* / *sociable*. You always get good marks in exams.
2 My sister gets nervous when she meets new people. She's quite *shy / tidy*.
3 I don't usually mind waiting. I'm quite *patient / confident*.
4 We're a bit *lazy / unsociable*. We prefer to be on our own.
5 Most people think my brother is *untidy / stupid*, but actually, he's really smart.
6 My partner enjoys her job and does it well. She's very *hard-working / honest*.
7 My husband likes having things in the right place. He's very *tidy / smart*.
8 Most of my friends are artists. They are all very *creative / quiet*.

PRONUNCIATION adjective word stress (3)

3a Underline the syllable which are stressed in the words in the box. Then complete the table.

~~clever~~ confident creative honest lazy patient sociable untidy

Oo	Ooo	oOo
clever		

b **6.1**))) Listen and check.

c **6.1**))) Listen again. Pause the CD and repeat after each word.

Grammar making comparisons

4 Complete the table with the comparative and superlative forms of the adjectives.

Adjective	Comparative adjective	Superlative adjective
1 bad	_worse_	the _____
2 good	_____	the _____
3 honest	_____	the _____
	less honest	the least honest
4 lazy	_____	the _____
5 old	_____	the _____
6 smart	_____	the _____
7 sociable	_____	the _____
	less sociable	the least sociable
8 tidy	_____	the _____

5 Write sentences using comparative or superlative adjectives.

1 fruit / healthy / chocolate
  Fruit is healthier than chocolate.

2 rugs / small / carpets
  _____

3 Monday / bad / day of the week
  _____

4 gold / expensive / plastic
  _____

5 I think / skiing / exciting / sport
  _____

6 they say flying / safe / way to travel
  _____

7 your English / good / mine
  _____

8 my hometown / lively / place I know
  _____

6 Rewrite the comparative sentences with (*not*) *as … as*. Use the adjectives in the box.

big dangerous dark ~~difficult~~ hard-working old thin wet

1 English is easier than Chinese.
  English _isn't as difficult as Chinese._

2 Today is drier than yesterday.
  Today _____

3 A duvet is thicker than a sheet.
  A duvet _____

4 My brother is lazier than me.
  He _____

5 Your hair is lighter than mine.
  Your hair _____

6 I'm younger than my wife.
  I'm _____

7 My office is smaller than yours.
  My office _____

8 Cars are safer than motorbikes.
  Cars _____

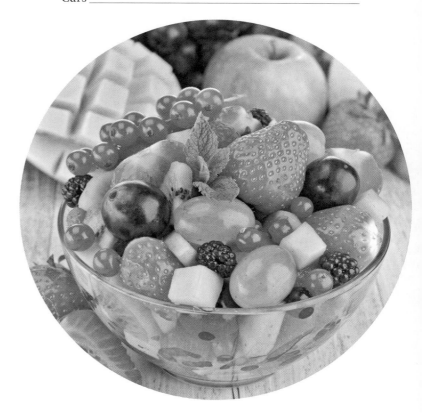

I can …	Very well	Quite well	More practice
describe character.	○	○	○
talk about similarities and differences.	○	○	○

6.2 A long way home

Vocabulary family

1 Complete the table with the correct family words.

Females	Males
aunt	1 _uncle_
2 _____	cousin
daughter	3 _____
4 _____	grandfather
great-grandmother	5 _____
6 _____	half-brother
mother-in-law	7 _____
8 _____	nephew
stepmother	9 _____

2 Complete the words in the conversations.

1 A Is that your boyfriend?
  B Yes, his name's Rashid. We're a c_ouple_ .

2 A Have you got any brothers or sisters?
  B No, I haven't. I'm an o_____ ch_____.

3 A Have you got a large family?
  B Yes, but I only see my r_____ at weddings.

4 A Has your friend left her husband?
  B Yes. They're going to g_____ d_____.

5 A You look exactly like your sister.
  B Yes, we're tw_____.

6 A Are you married?
  B No, I'm a s_____ p_____.

7 A How many children would you like?
  B Two or three. But I'd also like to a_____ one.

8 A Is your sister going out with Matt?
  B Yes. They're going to g_____ e_____
  next month.

3 Complete the article with the words in the box.

couples daughters get divorced grandfathers
only child relatives ~~single parent~~ uncles

Family facts around the world

Did you know ...?

- Children have a mother and a father who are their parents. However, more children live with a **1** _single parent_ in the Americas, Europe, Oceania and Africa than in the rest of the world. In these families, it is the oldest relatives, such as grandmothers and **2**_____, who help to look after the younger children.

- Children usually live with their parents and their brothers and sisters. Sharing a house with other **3**_____ is more common in Asia, the Middle East, South America and Africa. People in these areas often live with grandparents and great-grandparents, but some live with aunts and **4**_____, too.

- The main reason for finding a partner is usually to form a new family together. **5**_____ are more likely to be married in Africa, Asia and the Middle East. In the Americas, Europe and Oceania more people **6**_____ than in other places.

- Families in some countries have more children than families in others. It is unusual for African families to have an **7**_____. In Nigeria, women usually have five or six sons and **8**_____.

4a Circle the word with a different vowel sound.

1 son   mother   (adopt)
2 **au**nt   f**a**ther   p**a**rent
3 div**or**ced   c**ou**sin   **u**ncle
4 d**au**ghter   eng**a**ged   sister-in-l**aw**
5 c**ou**ple   h**u**sband   **o**nly

PRONUNCIATION family words

b 6.2))) Listen and check.

c 6.2))) Listen again. Pause the CD and repeat after each word.

40 | Oxford 3000™

Grammar present perfect simple and past simple

→ **STUDY TIP** The list of irregular verbs on p.166 of your Coursebook contains the past participle of these verbs, as well as the past simple forms. The past participle is in the third column of the list, and we use it to form the present perfect simple. As you did with the past simple forms, study five verbs every day until you remember the past participle forms of each verb on the list. This will make it easier for you to use the present perfect simple correctly.

5   Use the words to write present perfect simple sentences and questions.

1   my grandfather / give me / his old car
    My grandfather has given me his old car.

2   they / not hear / from their son this week
    _____

3   your friend / ever / speak / to her stepbrother?
    _____

4   I / never / meet / my cousins in Australia
    _____

5   my sister / find / a new boyfriend
    _____

6   we / not see / our great-grandparents recently
    _____

7   my mother-in-law / never / invite us / for a meal
    _____

8   you / ever / fall / down the stairs?
    _____

6   Choose the correct option to complete the sentences.

1   Have you ever lent money to your family?
    No, but I *'ve lent /*(lent) some to a friend last week.

2   Have you ever been camping?
    Yes, but we *haven't enjoyed / didn't enjoy* it last time.

3   Have you been on a plane?
    No, I *haven't flown / didn't fly* before.

4   Have you ever seen the Eiffel Tower?
    Yes, I *'ve lived / lived* in Paris when I was young.

5   Have you ever done yoga?
    Yes, I *'ve had / had* a yoga class yesterday.

6   Have you ever driven on the motorway?
    Yes, I *'ve done / did* it lots of times.

7   Have you ever been to China?
    No, but I *'ve been / went* to Japan a few years ago.

7   Complete the conversation with the correct present perfect simple or past simple form of the verb in brackets.

A ¹ _Have you ever done_ (you/ever/do) anything really exciting?

B Well, ² _____ (I/not/travel) into space, if that's what you mean! But, yes, ³ _____ (I/drive) a Ferrari.

A Really? When ⁴ _____ (you/do) that?

B Last year. ⁵ _____ (my girlfriend/give) me 30 minutes in a Ferrari as a present.

A How far ⁶ _____ (you/go)?

B ⁷ _____ (I/not/drive) very far – about 50 km.

A ⁸ _____ (you/enjoy) it?

B Yes, it was fun.

A What about your girlfriend? ⁹ _____ (she/ever/do) anything similar?

B Yes, she loves exciting sports and she often goes skiing and surfing. ¹⁰ _____ (she/climb) Everest too, and ¹¹ _____ (she/fly) a helicopter. But ¹² _____ (she/not/jump) out of a plane. I'm going to give her a parachute jump for her next birthday!

I can ...	Very well	Quite well	More practice
talk about family.	○	○	○
talk about experiences.	○	○	○

6.3 Vocabulary development

Vocabulary adjective prefixes

1 Complete the table with the opposite of the adjectives in the box.

> fair friendly happy healthy honest kind lucky
> necessary organized patient pleasant polite
> possible usual

dis-	un-	im-
	unfair	

2 Complete the conversations with eight words from exercise **1**.

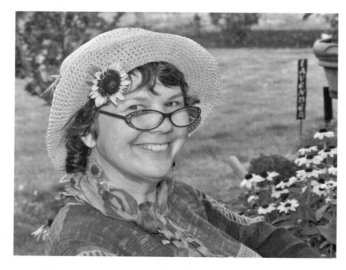

1 A Does anyone in your family wear strange clothes?
   B Yes, I've got an aunt who wears _unusual_ hats.
2 A Did you find the homework difficult?
   B I couldn't do it. It was _____.
3 A What do you do to keep fit?
   B Nothing. I'm really _____ at the moment.
4 A Does your niece tell lies?
   B Yes, she's a bit _____.

5 A Why are those children rude?
   B They're always _____.
6 A What's that horrible smell?
   B I don't know, but it's very _____.
7 A Is your husband tidy?
   B No, he's a bit _____.
8 A Why is your brother sad?
   B He's _____ because he's getting divorced.

Vocabulary review

3 Complete the table with the opposite adjectives for describing character.

> confident lazy sociable stupid untidy

Adjective	Opposite
clever/smart	¹ _stupid_
²_____	shy
hard-working	³_____
quiet	
⁴_____	unsociable
tidy	⁵_____

4 Complete the family words.

1 c**ousi**n
2 gr_ _t-gr_ndm_th_r
3 h_lf-s_st_r
4 n_ph_w
5 c_ _pl_
6 g_t _ng_g_d
7 r_l_t_v_s
8 tw_ns

5 Complete the table with the opposite form of the adjectives in the box.

> friendly healthy lucky organized pleasant polite

dis-	dishonest, ¹ _disorganized_
im-	impatient, ²_____, impossible
un-	unfair, ³_____, unhappy ⁴_____, unkind ⁵_____, unnecessary ⁶_____, unusual

6.4   Speaking and writing

Writing responding to news on social media

1 Circle the incorrect response.

1 **Tony**   Holiday cancelled. Not happy!
   Kristine *Bad luck! / I'm SO jealous! / Sorry to hear that.*

2 **Marta**   Just arrived at the airport. Barbados here we come!
   Sarah   *You lucky thing! / Have a fab time! / Get well soon.*

3 **Mary**   Great news – won my tennis match!
   John   *Congratulations! / Thinking of you. / Well done!*

4 **Jill**   Bad back – can't move!
   Stuart   *Get well soon. / Good luck! / Hope you feel better soon.*

5 **Doris**   My new niece – isn't she beautiful!
   Dominique *You'll be fine. / Great pic. / Love the pic!*

6 **Eldon**   Driving test tomorrow …
   Ania   *Best of luck! / Fingers crossed! / Well done!*

2 Complete the sentences with *just*, *already* or *yet*.

1 He's _____ left the office – if you run, you might see him in the car park.

2 They've _____ booked their flights to Goa in September, so you don't need to do it for them.

3 Have you seen the new Scarlet Johansson film _____ ?

4 He's _____ seen his exam results online, he doesn't need to go to the school.

Speaking giving and responding to news

3 Choose the correct options to complete the conversations.

Conversation 1

A Hey, Becky. [1] Guess what? / Never mind.

B What?

A I'm getting engaged!

B Congratulations! [2] *That's great news! / What a pity!*

A We're having a party on May 1st. Can you come?

B Yes, I'd love to. [3] *Oh dear. I'm sorry / I'm really happy for you.*

Conversation 2

A Hiya. Are you OK?

B No, not really. My grandfather's in hospital.

A [4] *Oh no! / Oh wow!* What's the problem?

B He fell over last night.

A [5] *Oh dear. I'm sorry. / How amazing!*

B He spent all night on the floor of the bathroom.

A [6] *That's wonderful! / What a shame!* What have the doctors said?

B I don't know yet. I'm going to visit him this evening.

A [7] *Never mind. / Guess what?* I'm sure he'll be OK.

4 Read the lines from two conversations. Decide if they belong to Conversation 1 or Conversation 2. Write *1* or *2*.

_1_ A Have you heard the news? About my sister and her husband?

_2_ A I've got some bad news for you, Danny.

____ B What?

____ B No. What?

____ A Tom and Alice are getting divorced.

____ A They're adopting a baby.

____ B That's terrible! What happened?

____ B How exciting! When are they getting him?

____ A They're going to get him next month.

____ A Tom moved out last week.

____ B Oh wow! I can't wait to see him!

____ B How awful! I'll call Alice tonight.

I can …	Very well	Quite well	More practice
understand and use adjective prefixes.	○	○	○
give and respond to news.	○	○	○
use the present perfect simple with *just*, *already* and *yet*.	○	○	○

6.5 Reading for pleasure

Little Rock

1   Look at the photo. What kind of discrimination does it show? Circle the correct answer 1, 2, 3 or 4.

1   age   3   religious
2   racial   4   sex

2   Read an extract from the biography of Martin Luther King.

3   Choose the correct options to complete the extract summary.

> There were problems in the South because the local population wanted the schools to be ¹*mixed / segregated.* Change started to come in the 1950s when the law changed ²*and black children wanted to go to Central High School / and white children wanted to go to another school.* On 2nd September Orval Faubus tried to ³*break the law / enforce the law.* Later in the same month ⁴*there were more protests outside Central High / everything calmed down.* The president ⁵*reacted to the situation / ignored the situation.* From then on the black children were protected ⁶*by soldiers / by police.*

4   Think about the racism in the story. Can you think of other countries in the world where racism has been an important issue? Do people worry about racism in your country? Why/Why not?

The story so far
Martin Luther King Junior (January 15th, 1929 – April 4th, 1968) was the leader of the African-American Civil Rights Movement. The incident in the extract took place just after he and his new wife moved back to the South of the United States.

Big trouble in Little Rock

There were many other things in the South that needed to change. Schools were segregated: white children went to all-white schools, black children went to all-black schools. Although there were more black children than white children in the South, much more money was spent on white schools than on black schools.

But in 1954 the law was changed. Now it was against the law to have different schools for black children and white children. The new law said that all schools had to take both black children and white children.

Change came slowly to the South. Many white people hated the new law, and in many Southern states, they refused to obey it. Arkansas was one of these states. In the state capital, Little Rock, nine black students tried to enter the Central High School at the start of the 1957–58 school year. Little Rock soon became one of the most famous places in the story of the fight for civil rights.

On 2 September, the night before the start of the new school year, the leader of the Arkansas government, Orval Faubus, ordered the National Guard to stand outside Central High School. He told them to stop any black student from entering the school, because he was afraid of trouble from protesters. The school was closed. But a judge said that Faubus could not use the National Guard to do something that was against the law. On 23 September the Little Rock police took the nine black students into Central High. A crowd of more than a thousand white people tried to stop the black students from entering. The crowd rioted and attacked the police. The pictures of the riot were seen all over the world, and many Americans were shocked to see such ugly attacks in their own country. Next day, the President of the United States, Dwight D. Eisenhower, ordered the army to Little Rock. A thousand soldiers entered Little Rock Central High School. Every morning the nine black children walked to the school, and every morning the soldiers protected them as they walked through crowds of angry whites.

Text extract from *Oxford Bookworms Readers: Little Rock*

Review: Units 5 and 6

Grammar

1 Choose the correct option to complete the sentences.

1 Alaska is the *larger / largest / most large / least large* state in the USA.

2 There weren't *any / little / much / some* black US presidents before Barack Obama.

3 We *go / has been / have been / went* to Disneyland last year.

4 You'll need *any / some / much / a little* American dollars if you're going to the US.

5 The United States was *a / an / - / the* country with problems in the 1950s and 1960s.

6 *Are / Did / Do / Have* you ever been to San Francisco?

7 New York is *more / most / as / less* important than Little Rock.

2 Complete the text. Write one word in each space.

> Mahatma Gandhi is one of the ¹ *most* famous human rights leaders who has ever lived. There are few people who ² _____ never heard of him. Gandhi was born in India in 1869, but after university he went to London to become ³ _____ lawyer. From there he went to South Africa, where he tried to help ⁴ _____ Indian immigrants who lived there. During his twenty years in South Africa, he went to prison ⁵ _____ times, but in the end conditions got better. Gandhi returned home in 1915, but the situation in India was almost as bad ⁶ _____ in South Africa because India had a British government. Gandhi protested against the British, but he was never violent. Soon ⁷ _____ of people were following him. The British left India in 1947, but Gandhi was assassinated the following year. Since then, his birthday has ⁸ _____ a national holiday in India.

Vocabulary

3 Circle the word that is different.

1 metal cash leather plastic

2 lend owe adopt borrow

3 antique confident lazy sociable

4 only child bank account half-sister single

5 engaged special useful valuable

6 balance change uncle rent

7 smart tidy creative divorced

4 Complete the text with the words in the box.

> amount comfortable couple ~~ordinary~~ patient pay for quiet son

> Aung San Suu Kyi is no ¹ *ordinary* woman. Because of her ideas, she spent more than twenty years of her life under house arrest at her home in Myanmar. Towards the end, her house was not very ² _____ because she had no electricity. But Ms Suu Kyi was ³ _____ and today she is free. She was born in Myanmar in 1945, but she went to university in Oxford, England, where she met her husband. The ⁴ _____ got married in 1972 and had their first ⁵ _____ in 1973. Ms Suu Kyi returned to Myanmar in 1988 to look after her mother, who was ill, and she stayed to protest against the government. The country's leaders put her under house arrest because they wanted her to be ⁶ _____. In 1991, Ms Suu Kyi received the Nobel Peace Prize for her work, which came with a large ⁷ _____ of money.

5 Complete the sentences with the correct form of the words in brackets.

1 The staff in that shop are very *unfriendly* . (friendly)

2 Moving house can be very _____ . (stress)

3 That was very _____ of you to take that money without asking. (honest)

4 Is this film _____ for children to watch? (suit)

5 The party was a _____ – nobody enjoyed it. (disappoint)

6 I keep all my most valuable _____ on my chest of drawers. (possess)

Speaking

6 Put the words in the correct order to make sentences.

1 forgotten / English / the / in / I've / word
   I've forgotten the word in English.

2 really / you / happy / I'm / for
   _____

3 you / news / heard / Have / the
   _____

4 what / for / I'm / That's / looking
   _____

5 open / use / doors / it / You / to
   _____

7 Travel

7.1 On the move

transport

1 Match the two halves of the sentences.

1 It's safer to cross the main
  a advance so they were less expensive.

2 I can only use my bus
  b jam on the way to work.

3 Do you go to work by public
  c road at the lights.

4 We bought our tickets in
  d pass to travel in the city centre.

5 I got caught in a huge traffic
  e transport or by car?

2 Replace the words in **bold** with the words in the box.

> convenient crowded fare fuel ~~greener~~ pollution
> reliable

1 Riding a bike is **better for the environment** than going by car. _greener_

2 The **dirty air** in the city centre is quite bad this morning. _____

3 The station was **full of people** because the train was late. _____

4 What **petrol or diesel** does your car use? _____

5 The bus service in my town isn't very **regular and efficient**. _____

6 If you live near a station, the metro is very **easy and quick to use**. _____

7 How much is the **money you pay to travel** from Paris to London by train? _____

3 Complete the article with the words in the box.

> convenient crowded fare greener main roads
> public transport reliable ~~traffic jams~~

Getting around in Moscow

Moscow is one of the worst cities in the world for driving and drivers sit for more than twenty days a year in ¹ _traffic jams_ in the Russian capital. The ²_____ of the city centre are busiest during the early morning rush hour, which lasts from 8 a.m. to 11 a.m., so many residents leave their cars at home and use ³_____ instead. The Moscow metro is the most ⁴_____ way to get around the city because it is quick, cheap and easy to use. Metro entrances are marked with a large red letter 'M' and the ⁵_____ is cheaper if you buy a ticket for ten or twenty rides. Some of the stations are beautiful, such as Mayakovskaya Station, to the north of the green line. The trains are generally ⁶_____ and passengers hardly ever have to wait for more than three minutes. However, up to nine million people a day use the metro so it can get very ⁷_____ when people are travelling to and from work. There are also buses in Moscow, but the metro is much faster – and ⁸_____ – than the bus.

Grammar   prediction (*will, might*)

4   Complete the conversations with the contraction of *will* +
the verbs in the box.

<del>be</del>   have   park   pass   rain   win

1   **A**   Will you be home for dinner?
    B   No, I *'ll be* late.
2   **A**   My wife is taking her driving test today.
    B   I'm sure she _____.
3   **A**   We're going to a party tonight.
    B   I know you _____ a good time.
4   **A**   What will we do if we can't find a parking space?
    B   We _____ in the car park.
5   **A**   Why have you got an umbrella?
    B   Because I think it _____.
6   **A**   Is your team good?
    B   Yes, but I don't think they _____.

PRONUNCIATION   *might*

5a   **7.1**))) Listen to two sentences with *might*. Notice that when
    might is stressed, you sound less sure.
    I might buy a car. (= quite sure)
    I might buy a car. (= not very sure)

b   **7.1**))) Listen again. Pause the CD and repeat after each
    sentence.

c   **7.2**))) Listen to five more sentences and decide if they are
    'quite sure' or 'not very sure'.
    1   *quite sure* _____
    2   _____
    3   _____
    4   _____
    5   _____

6   Choose the correct option to complete the sentences.
    1   I told him it's my birthday next week, but I know he
        might / 'll forget.
    2   Let's take a map. We *might /* 'll get lost.
    3   I'm not sure about that film. You *might not / won't*
        like it.
    4   The flight is too expensive. I probably *might not / won't*
        have enough money.
    5   We're not sure how we're getting home. We *might /* 'll
        take a taxi.
    6   We invited my grandparents to the party, but I don't
        think they *might /* 'll come.
    7   It's very late. We probably *might not / won't* arrive
        on time.
    8   I don't know what to do tonight. I *might not / won't*
        go out.

7   Complete the text with *will* or *might* and the
    verbs in brackets.

▶ **Mars One**

Mars One is an amazing project that is sending a group
of people to live on the planet Mars. The first four
astronauts **1** _will leave_ (leave) Earth in April 2024
to start the 210-day journey to the Red Planet. They
2 _____ (not see) their family and
friends again because the trip is only one way. Everybody
knows that the journey **3** _____ (be)
dangerous and the astronauts **4** _____
(not arrive) on Mars safely. Let's hope they are lucky
and they land without any problems. Living on Mars
will be very different from living on Earth because they
5 _____ (spend) all of their time
inside. They **6** _____ (not meet)
any different people for the next two years, so
it's possible they **7** _____
(feel) bored. However, a second group of
astronauts **8** _____
(join) the first group in 2026 so they
will have more people to talk to. Mars
One is planning to make a reality
show about the project, and the
organizers are sure that everybody
on Earth **9** _____
(watch) the astronauts land on Mars. It
10 _____ (be) interesting
to see what they think about their new home
and their new lives.

I can ...	Very well	Quite well	More practice
talk about transport.	○	○	○
make predictions.	○	○	○

7.2 Getting away

Vocabulary holidays

1 Match definitions 1–8 to words in the box.

> accommodation culture ~~flight~~ guidebook insurance
> research reviews souvenir

1 a journey by air _flight_
2 a place to live or stay _____
3 a thing that you buy to remind you of your holiday
   _____
4 an agreement with a company that will pay your costs if
   you have an accident, etc. _____
5 pages full of information for tourists _____
6 the study of something to find out more information
   _____
7 the customs and ideas of a country _____
8 opinions about hotels and restaurants, etc. _____

2 Complete the phrases with the correct verbs in the box.

> ~~buy~~ experience explore get go lie read try

What can you do …

1 in a shop the day before you go home?
   buy souvenirs
2 on a nice day in a hotel? _____ by the pool
3 in a bank before you travel? _____ foreign
   currency
4 in a restaurant or at a street stall? _____ the
   local food
5 in the airport or on the plane? _____ a guidebook
6 in a very beautiful city? _____ sightseeing
7 at a market or a festival? _____ the local culture
8 in a car you hire for a few days? _____ the area

3 Match words from A to words from B to make verb phrases.
Then complete the article with the verb phrases.

> **A** apply ~~book~~ buy choose hire read
>
> **B** a car for a visa online reviews travel insurance
> your accommodation ~~your flight~~

Online holidays

Technology has changed the way we do everything,
especially when it comes to organizing a summer
holiday. You no longer need to go to a travel agency
because you can do everything yourself on the internet.
Many airlines have websites where you can **¹** _book
your flight_ and these companies usually offer extra
services, too. If you are worried about losing your
possessions, you can often **²**_____
from the company you fly with. If the place you are
staying in is far from the airport, you might want to
³_____ to get there. When you have
got your flight, you need to **⁴**_____.
The best way to do this is to **⁵**_____
for each of the hotels you are interested in. These will
give you an idea of the location and quality of the hotel.
The internet will also tell you if you need anything
special for your trip, like a visa. While it might not be
possible to **⁶**_____ online, there are
websites that will tell you which documents you need
and where to go to get one. The internet has made it
much easier to organize a holiday and it has also made
it a lot cheaper.

PRONUNCIATION stress in phrases

4a <u>Underline</u> the unstressed syllables in the phrases.

1 book <u>your</u> flight   5 read a guidebook
2 lie by the pool   6 apply for a visa
3 try the local food   7 go sightseeing
4 hire a car   8 explore the area

b **7.3**))) Listen and check.

c **7.3**))) Listen again. Pause the CD and repeat after each word.

Grammar *something, anyone, everybody, nowhere,* etc.

5 Complete definitions 1–8 with *something, anyone, everybody, nowhere,* etc for the words in **bold**. In some cases there are two possible answers.

1 It's _somewhere_ you go to relax in the summer. **pool**

2 It's how you feel when you've learned _____ quickly. **clever**

3 It's a thing you use on public transport to go _____ more cheaply. **bus pass**

4 It's an adjective for a seat where _____ wants to sit. **comfortable**

5 It's a thing you use when _____ is clean. **cloth**

6 It's an adjective for a person who doesn't say _____. **quiet**

7 It's how you feel when you haven't got _____ to talk to. **lonely**

8 It's an adjective to describe a place where _____ can move because there are too many people. **crowded**

6 Choose the correct options to complete the text.

Beautiful Krakow

If you're looking for ¹*anywhere / everywhere / somewhere* interesting to go for your next holiday, why not try Krakow in Poland? The city is more than 750 years old, and ²*anywhere / nowhere / somewhere* in Poland is more historical. The most famous attractions are the Wawel Castle and the beautiful Old Town, with its enormous market place. There isn't ³*anything / nothing / something* more relaxing than sitting in the square, enjoying a cup of coffee. Walking through the narrow streets of the city, you'll find ⁴*anything / everything / something* old, strange or amazing around every corner.

To see ⁵*anything / everything / nothing* in the city you need to spend at least a week there, but you should choose your time to visit carefully. ⁶*Anybody / Everybody / Somebody* goes to Krakow in the summer, so from June to September, you might not find ⁷*anywhere / everywhere / somewhere* to stay.

⁸*Anyone / No one / Someone* who visits Krakow is disappointed with their holiday.

I can …	Very well	Quite well	More practice
talk about holidays.	○	○	○
use *something, anyone, everybody, nowhere,* etc.	○	○	○

7.3 Vocabulary development

Vocabulary -ed and -ing adjectives

→ **STUDY TIP** *-ed* adjectives are formed from verbs and they follow the same rules as regular past simple forms. When the infinitive of the verb ends in /t/ or /d/, it has an extra syllable /ɪd/ in the past tense.

1 Tick (✔) the sentences that are correct and put a cross (✗) if they are wrong. Correct the incorrect sentences.

1 Paris is one of my favourite cities. The Eiffel Tower is amazing. ✔

2 I fell down the stairs. It was really embarrassed. ✗ *embarrassing*

3 The film was really disappointed. We didn't really enjoy it. _____

4 I'm really exciting about my sister's news. She's getting engaged! _____

5 There was a terrible storm last night. I was really frightened. _____

6 I heard some surprised news. I didn't expect it. _____

7 My neighbour called the police. He was worried about his son. _____

8 You look very relaxing. Have you been on holiday? _____

2 Complete the adjectives with *-ed* or *-ing*.

1 A Why do you always go to the swimming pool?
   B Because I find it very relax*ing*.

2 A Why aren't you talking to your boyfriend?
   B Because I'm annoy_____ with him.

3 A Why did your friends go to bed?
   B Because they were tir_____.

4 A Why are you watching that documentary again?
   B Because it's fascinat_____.

5 A Why did you run out of the room?
   B Because I was embarrass_____.

6 A Why are you looking at me like that?
   B Because I'm amaz_____ that you passed.

7 A Why won't your girlfriend watch the football?
   B Because she thinks it's bor_____.

8 A Why can't you do the homework?
   B Because I'm confus_____.

Vocabulary review

3 Complete the transport words in the table.

advance jams pass ~~road~~ transport

Car	Bus / Train
fuel	bus 3 _____
main 1 _road_	convenient
pollution	crowded
traffic 2 _____	fare
	greener
	in 4 _____
	public 5 _____
	reliable

4 Match verbs 1–7 to words a–g to make verb phrases.

1 apply   a the area
2 buy   b for a visa
3 choose   c by the pool
4 explore   d your accommodation
5 go   e online reviews
6 lie   f travel insurance
7 read   g sightseeing

5 Complete the *-ed* and *-ing* adjectives.

1 amazed / ing
2 b_red / ing
3 d_s_pp_ _nted / ing
4 _xc_ted / ing
5 fr_ght_ned / ing
6 s_rpr_sed / ing
7 w_rried / ying
8 _nn_yed / ing
9 c_nf_sed / ing
10 _mb_rrassed / ing
11 f_sc_nated / ing
12 r_l_xed / ing

7.4   Speaking and writing

Speaking checking into a hotel

1a Put the conversation in the right order 1–11.

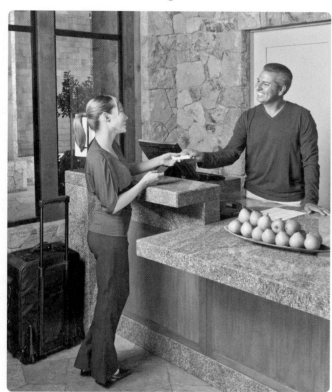

____ Thanks a lot.

____ You have to vacate your room by 10.30.

____ OK, Ms Genieva. So that's a single room just for one night.

_1_ Hi, I'd like to check in, please.

____ Right. Is there anywhere I can leave my luggage tomorrow?

____ Yeah, that's right.

____ Yes, my name's Tatiana Genieva.

____ Could you fill in the registration form, please?

____ Yes, of course. Do you have a reservation?

____ Yeah, sure. Just one question. What time is check-out?

____ Yes, you can leave it behind reception.

b 7.4 》) Listen and check your answers to exercise **1a**.

2 Complete the conversation with the phrases in the box.

~~Could we check in, please?~~   I'll get someone to help you with your luggage.   Is Wi-Fi available in the room?   Is there a charge for it?   What was the name again, please?

A Hi. **¹** _Could we check in, please?_

B Yes, of course. What's the name, please?

A Anders. We have a reservation for four nights.

B **²** _____

A Anders. That's A-N-D-E-R-S.

B Right, Mr Anders. You're in Room 304. Here's your key card.

A Thanks. Just a few questions.
   3 _____

B Yes, it is.

A Right.
   4 _____

B No, it's free of charge to all our guests.

A Thanks. Can you tell me where the lift is?

B Yes, it's through those doors.
   5 _____

A Thank you.

Writing   **short notes and messages**

3 Put the words in the correct order to make short notes or messages.

1 text / your / for / Thanks / . / feeling / Am / better / much
   Thanks for your text. Am feeling much better.

2 work / Just / left / . / pizzas / me / Want / to get / some / dinner / for ?
   _____

3 traffic jam / in / Stuck / a / . / meeting / Will / late / be / for .
   _____

4 order / out / Lift / of / . / stairs / Use .
   _____

5 you / See / airport / at / Fri / on / . / 6.30 / lands / at / Plane .
   _____

6 client / Am / with / . / call / back / Will / mins / in / 15 .
   _____

I can …	Very well	Quite well	More practice
understand and use -ed and -ing adjectives.	◯	◯	◯
check into a hotel.	◯	◯	◯
write short notes and messages.	◯	◯	◯

Language and learning

8.1 The amazing human brain

Grammar ability (*can, be able to*)

1a Replace the words in **bold** using *be able to*.

1 **My sister can't walk** because she has broken her leg.
   _My sister isn't able to walk because she has broken
   her leg._

2 **Can you lend me some money** to go to a concert?
   _____

3 **I can drive** but I haven't got a car.
   _____

4 **We can see the sea** from the window of our room.
   _____

5 **Can your boyfriend speak** any foreign languages?
   _____

6 I'm tired because **I can't sleep at night**.
   _____

PRONUNCIATION *to* in *be able to*

b **8.1**)) Listen and check. Notice the weak /tə/ pronunciation of *to* in each sentence.

c **8.1**)) Listen again. Pause the CD and repeat after each sentence.

2 Complete the sentences with *can* or *can't* where possible. If not, use *be able to* in the correct form.

1 I _can_ cook, but not as well as my mother.
2 I _____ finish your book by the end of the week, I'm sorry.
3 My nephew _____ play chess very well – he has won several competitions.
4 My grandparents _____ use a computer. They have never learnt.
5 Oh no, it's raining! We _____ have a barbecue tonight.
6 We _____ afford to go on a holiday this year, because we haven't got enough money.

3 Complete the text with *can, can't* or the correct form of *be able to* with the verbs in brackets.

Preparing for the future

Scientists say that there are many ways we [1] _can keep_ (keep) our brains healthy, so that we [2] _____ (have) a normal life when we are older.

Learn a new activity

Think of something that you [3] _____ (not do) but you would like to learn: another language perhaps, or a musical instrument. Learning something new exercises your brain, so that you [4] _____ (deal) better with new situations in the future.

Do some exercise

A healthy body means a healthy brain. Doctors say that regular exercise might [5] _____ (stop) the brain getting ill with Alzheimer's, for example. People who don't go walking, running or swimming might have problems in later life because they [6] _____ (sleep).

Have fun

Going out with friends and spending time with relatives [7] _____ (make) you feel more positive about life. As you grow older, you will do different things together, but if you have friends, you [8] _____ (phone) someone for a chat at any time of the day.

Listen to the silence

You don't have to be active all of the time, and it is important to find a moment when you [9] _____ (relax). Our brains need time to rest, as well as our bodies, so that we don't feel stressed. This also prepares us for the future, when we [10] _____ (not go out) every day.

Vocabulary skills and abilities

4 Complete the table with the phrases in the box.

| I'm brilliant   I'm good   I'm not very good   ~~I'm OK~~ |
| I'm quite good   I'm really good   I'm very good |
| I'm terrible   I'm useless |

+ + + +		
+ + +		
+ +		
+	I'm OK	
–		
– –		

5 Use the words to write sentences.

1 My girlfriend / quite good / make speeches.
   My girlfriend is quite good at making speeches.

2 You / very good / tell jokes.
   _____

3 She / brilliant / organize events.
   _____

4 I / not very good / solve computer problems.
   _____

5 My husband / terrible / remember people's names.
   _____

6 They / good / spell.
   _____

7 I / OK / follow instructions.
   _____

8 We / useless / make decisions.
   _____

9 My daughter / really good / learn langauges.
   _____

10 I / useless / telling jokes.
   _____

6 Complete paragraphs 1–4 with the adjectives in brackets and the correct form of the verbs in the box. Then match the paragraphs to the photos a–d. Write the letter of the photo in the space.

| explain fix follow give learn make organize |
| ~~remember~~ solve take tell understand |

1 He's *quite good at remembering* people's names (quite good), but he _____ computer problems (useless). He _____ things clearly (very good). Photo ___

2 She _____ events (good), but she _____ languages (not very good). She _____ speeches (very good). Photo ___

3 He _____ how things work (very good) and he _____ directions (OK). He _____ things that are broken (really good). Photo ___

4 She _____ instructions (quite good) but she _____ jokes (terrible). She _____ care of people (brilliant). Photo ___

I can …	Very well	Quite well	More practice
talk about ability.	◯	◯	◯
talk about skills and abilities.	◯	◯	◯

The secrets of a successful education

Vocabulary & Speaking education

1 Complete the crossword with school subjects.

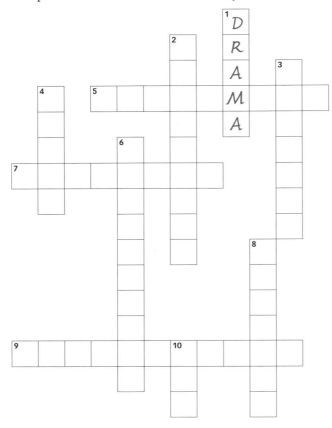

1 Students learn about plays and theatre in _drama_.
2 They study _____ like French and German, etc.
3 They learn about the physical world and nature in _____.
4 They study numbers, quantities and shapes in _____.
5 They learn about business and industry in _____.
6 They read different books in _____.
7 They play different sports in _____ education.
8 They learn about the past in _____.
9 They learn about computers in _____ technology.
10 They learn how to draw and paint in _____.

2 Complete the words in the sentences.
1 How often did you _take_ ex_ams_ when you were at school?
2 My brother loves travelling, so he'd like to tr_____ as a tour guide.
3 What qu_____ do you need if you want to be a lawyer?
4 Are you going to do a M_____ d_____ when you finish your course?
5 My teachers were very r_____ about homework and we only did it if we wanted to.
6 You have to get good gr_____ if you want to go to university.
7 I'm fascinated by the brain, so I'd like to study ps_____.
8 Parents don't have to pay to send their child to a st_____ sch_____.
9 My partner is studying at college for a d_____ in hotel management.

3 Complete the article with the words in the box.

career   degree   do well   education   ~~private school~~
strict   success   uniform

Big is beautiful

With 47,000 students, City Montessori School in India is the largest school in the world. Parents pay £12 a month for younger students and £30 for older ones, which makes it a ¹ _private school_. The school rules are quite ²_____, and students have to wear a ³_____. Dr Jagdish Gandhi and Dr Bharti Ghandhi started the school in 1959, because they believed that all children have a right to an ⁴_____. Students say that they have to work very hard to ⁵_____, because there are a lot of students in each class. Most classes have between 40 and 50 students, but the teachers are happy with that number. As well as subjects such as Maths and English, students at City Montessori School learn about world peace. People in the local area like the school's philosophy, which is one of the reasons for its ⁶_____. On leaving school, some students have gone to do a ⁷_____ at Harvard University in the USA, while others have started a ⁸_____ at the United Nations.

Grammar obligation, necessity and permission (*must, have to, can*)

PRONUNCIATION *can/can't*

4a **8.2**))) Listen to the sentences and <u>underline</u> the words that are stressed.

1 You can <u>*use*</u> the <u>*internet*</u> .
2 You can't take photos.
3 You can sit here.
4 You can't walk on the grass.
5 You can pay by credit card.
6 You can't play football here.

b **8.2**))) Listen again. Pause the CD and repeat after each sentence. Pay attention to the weak /kən/ pronunciation of *can* and the strong /ka:nt/ pronunciation of *can't*.

5 Choose the correct option to complete the sentences. In some sentences both answers may be possible.

1 We *don't have to* / *mustn't* go to work tomorrow. It's a holiday.
2 I'm late for a meeting. I *have to* / *must* go now.
3 Don't worry about the bill. We *can* / *must* pay by credit card.
4 There's a red flag. We *can't* / *mustn't* go swimming.
5 You *don't have to* / *mustn't* touch the cooker. It's hot.
6 You *can* / *have to* drive on the left in the UK.
7 You *must* / *have to* wear a seatbelt when you travel by car.
8 I *can't* / *don't have to* send personal emails from work.

6 Complete the article with the correct form of *must, have to* or *can* and the verbs in brackets. Sometimes there is more than one possible correct answer.

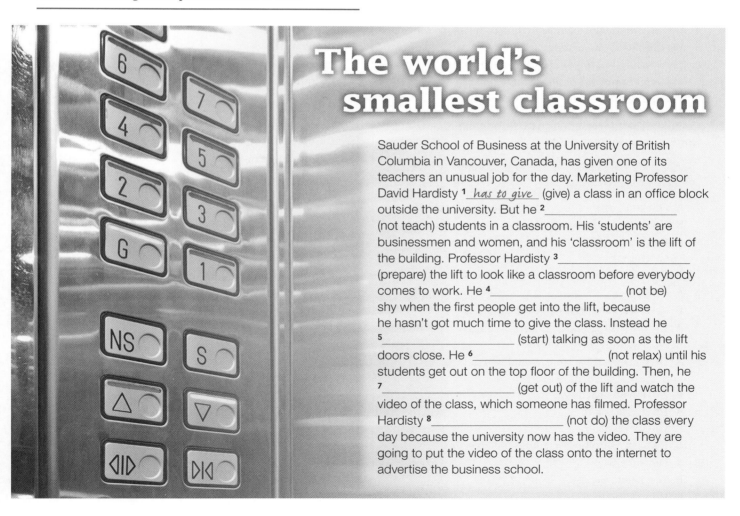

The world's smallest classroom

Sauder School of Business at the University of British Columbia in Vancouver, Canada, has given one of its teachers an unusual job for the day. Marketing Professor David Hardisty ¹ <u>*has to give*</u> (give) a class in an office block outside the university. But he ² _____ (not teach) students in a classroom. His 'students' are businessmen and women, and his 'classroom' is the lift of the building. Professor Hardisty ³ _____ (prepare) the lift to look like a classroom before everybody comes to work. He ⁴ _____ (not be) shy when the first people get into the lift, because he hasn't got much time to give the class. Instead he ⁵ _____ (start) talking as soon as the lift doors close. He ⁶ _____ (not relax) until his students get out on the top floor of the building. Then, he ⁷ _____ (get out) of the lift and watch the video of the class, which someone has filmed. Professor Hardisty ⁸ _____ (not do) the class every day because the university now has the video. They are going to put the video of the class onto the internet to advertise the business school.

I can …	Very well	Quite well	More practice
talk about education.	○	○	○
talk about obligation, necessity and permission.	○	○	○

8.3 Vocabulary development

Vocabulary *make* and *do*

→ **STUDY TIP** Have a page in your vocabulary notebook for phrases with *make* and another for phrases with *do*. Each time you come across a new phrase with *make* or *do*, write it on the correct page. You could also make cards and test yourself from time to time. This will make it easier for you to remember which verb to use.

1 Choose the correct option to complete the sentences.

1 I *do* / *make* my English homework the night before the class.

2 Do you know where I can *do* / *make* a photocopy?

3 When was the last time you *did* / *made* an exam?

4 He *did* / *made* the exercise wrong so he has to repeat it.

5 We didn't *do* / *make* much money when we sold our car.

6 My partner is *doing* / *making* a job he hates.

7 My neighbours *did* / *made* a lot of noise last night.

8 I hope I've *done* / *made* the right decision.

2 Complete the conversations with *do* or *make* and the words or phrases in the box.

> a course   a list   a mistake   a salad   friends   housework
> nothing   well   your bed

1 A Did you _do a course_ in science at university?
  B No, I studied languages.

2 A Do you _____ before you go shopping?
  B Yes, I always write down what I have to buy.

3 A Do you _____ every morning?
  B Yes, I do it as soon as I get up.

4 A Do you ever _____ for lunch?
  B No, I usually have a sandwich.

5 A Do you ever have time to sit down and _____?
  B No, I'm always busy.

6 A How easy is it to _____ where you live?
  B It's easy. Everybody is really sociable.

7 A Do you always _____ in exams?
  B Yes, I usually pass.

8 A How often do you _____ in an email?
  B Quite often. I'm not very good at spelling.

9 A When do you usually _____?
  B I always clean my flat at the weekend.

Vocabulary review

3 Match words 1–7 to words a–g to form abilities.

1 explaining   a languages
2 following   b events
3 learning   c instructions
4 making   d things clearly
5 organizing   e jokes
6 solving   f speeches
7 telling   g computer problems

4 Complete the expressions for 'doing well' and 'doing badly'.

> ~~brilliant~~   good   OK   really   terrible

doing well
be [1] _brilliant_ at
be (quite / [3]_____ /
very) good at
be [5]_____ at

doing badly
be [2]_____ / useless at
be not very [4]_____ at

5 Complete the missing vowels.

school subjects
1 _a_rt drama
2 _c_n_m_cs
3 _T (_nf_rm_t_ _n t_chn_l_gy)
4 P_ (phys_c_l _d_c_t_ _n)

education
5 d_pl_m_
6 M_st_r's d_gr_ _
7 qu_l_f_c_t_ _ns
8 s_cc_ss
9 _n_f_rm

6 Complete the table with the words in the box.

> ~~business~~   a decision   an exam   friends   homework
> a job   a list   money   a phone call   well/badly

do	make
[1] _business_	[6] _____
[2] _____	[7] _____
[3] _____	[8] _____
[4] _____	[9] _____
[5] _____	[10] _____

8.4   Speaking and writing

Speaking asking for clarification

1 Match sentences and questions 1–6 to responses a–f.

1 Sorry, what did you say?   a Nothing. I'll explain later.
2 What do you mean by   b Never mind. I'll draw you
   'a problem'?   a map.
3 Sorry, I keep losing   c I said, I'm going to be late.
   the signal.
4 I'm afraid I can't follow   d I said, do you come here
   your directions.   often?
5 Sorry, what was that?   e Can I call back later?
6 Sorry, I'm a bit confused.   f Don't worry. I'll say it
                                      again.

2a Complete the conversation with the phrases in the box.

> a really bad connection   breaking up   could you speak up
> I'm a bit lost   ~~Pardon~~   Please could you explain
> repeat that please   noisy in here

A Raz? Where are you?
B Hi, Amara. I'm on my way.
A ¹ _Pardon_ ?
B I'm on my way.
A Sorry, it's too
   ² _____ .
   Are you on your way? The
   party started an hour ago.

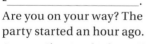

B Amara, I'm nearly there. But
   I've forgotten your address.
A Sorry, Raz. You're ³_____ . Can you
   remember my address?
B No, that's the problem.
A Raz, please ⁴_____ ?
B OK. IS THAT BETTER?
A Yes, that's much better. I said can you remember my
   address? It's number 107.
B Could you ⁵_____ ?
A 1-0-7. A hundred and seven South View Avenue.
B Right. ⁶_____ how to get there from
   the bus stop?

A OK. When you get off the bus, walk up the hill and take
   the second right.
B Amara, this is ⁷_____ .
A Up the hill and second right. Did you get that?
B Sorry, ⁸_____ .
A Raz. Raz? He's gone.

b **8.3**))) Listen and check your answers to the conversation in
   exercise **2a**.

Writing completing a form

3 Complete the form with the words in the box.

> Date of birth   Forename   Gender   Marital status
> Next of kin   Occupation   Place of birth   Signature
> Surname   ~~Title~~

¹ _Title_	Ms
² _____	Larsson
³ _____	Agnetha
⁴ _____	Female
⁵ _____	22.09.1966
⁶ _____	Stockholm, Sweden
⁷ _____	Married
⁸ _____	Doctor
⁹ _____	Bjorn Larsson (husband)
10 _____	Agnetha Larsson

I can …	Very well	Quite well	More practice
use *make* and *do*.	○	○	○
understand connected speech.	○	○	○
ask for clarification.	○	○	○
complete a form.	○	○	○

8.5 Listening for pleasure

Frightening experiences

1 Label the photos with the words in the box.

fire   landing   passengers   ~~roundabout~~   snow

1 roundabout

2 _____

3 _____

4 _____

5 _____

2 **8.4**))) Listen to seven speakers describing their most frightening experience.

3 **8.4**))) Listen again and complete the summaries.

> Speaker 1 was frightened because of the weather. She was going to visit her ¹ _mother-in-law_ and it was ² _____.

> Speaker 2 was travelling by ³ _____. He nearly had an accident with a ⁴ _____ at a roundabout.

> Speaker 3 was staying at a ⁵ _____. She had to leave her room because there was a ⁶ _____.

> Speaker 4 was travelling by ⁷ _____. He was frightened because the pilot couldn't ⁸ _____.

> Speaker 5 was sitting on a ⁹ _____. Another passenger made her give him her ¹⁰ _____.

> Speaker 6 was ¹¹ _____ in the sea. One of his friends told him not to ¹² _____.

> Speaker 7 was frightened by her ¹³ _____ having problems eating. Luckily, her ¹⁴ _____ helped.

4 Think about the speakers' frightening experiences again – which one did you think was the most scary? Why?

Review: Units 7 and 8

Grammar

1 Complete the sentences with one word. Sometimes more than one answer may be possible.

1 I was late for work this morning because I _couldn't_ start my car.

2 I don't know how I'm getting home, but I _____ get a taxi.

3 _____ is going on holiday, so there's a lot of traffic.

4 I'm sure your parents _____ enjoy their holiday – they love the beach.

5 You _____ park here because there is a 'No parking' sign.

6 I'm not doing _____ special this weekend.

7 We were _____ to find some cheap flights on the internet.

8 You _____ have a visa to enter the USA.

2 Choose the correct options to complete the text.

> Public transport is getting more expensive **1** *anywhere / everywhere / nowhere / somewhere* in the world, but the metro of Beijing is doing **2** *anything / everything / nothing / something* that will make it much cheaper. In the stations of line 10, there are some brand new machines where passengers **3** *can / might / must / will* pay the fare with empty water bottles. To use the machine, you **4** *can / might / must / will* have a Beijing transport pass and at least one plastic bottle. For each recycled bottle, the machine **5** *can / might / must / will* put a small amount of money on the pass. You **6** *are able / can / have / must* to wait about 20 seconds for the machine to do its job, which **7** *can / have to / might / must* be too long for passengers on their way to work.

Vocabulary

3 Complete the sentences with a suitable word.

1 The underground is very c_rowded_ in the morning and you can never get a seat.

2 My sister is very good at l_____ l_____, so she wants to be an interpreter.

3 Do you ever b_____ s_____ to help you remember your holiday?

4 My boyfriend is u_____ at remembering people's names.

5 Do you g_____ f_____ c_____ at the airport or from a bank?

4 Complete the article with the phrases in the box.

> fuel   greener   lie by the pool   organizing events   ~~pollution~~   science   trained

> Flying causes a lot of **1** _pollution_, but that doesn't stop people going abroad when they want to **2**_____ of a hotel for a week. But now two Swiss scientists have designed a plane that they hope will help save the planet. Bertrand Piccard and Andre Borschberg were both fascinated by **3**_____ when they were at school, and they soon started building their own planes. They have both **4**_____ as pilots to be able to fly their inventions. Their latest model, Solar Impulse 2, gets its energy from the sun, which makes it much **5**_____ than other planes. It flies without using any **6**_____ at all. Piccard and Borschberg are planning to test their plane soon. They are also **7**_____ to teach people about this clean technology.

5 Choose the correct option to complete the sentences.

1 What's wrong with your car? It's *doing / making* a strange noise.

2 Were you *frightened / frightening* during the storm?

3 What has been the most *embarrassed / embarrassing* moment of your life?

4 What's the most interesting course you have ever *done / made*?

5 Did you *do / make* friends easily when you were a child?

Speaking

6 Complete the conversation with the phrases in the box.

> could we check in, please   is Wi-Fi available in the room
> could you fill in the registration form, please
> ~~Do you have a reservation~~
> what do you mean by 'electronic device'

A Good morning. **1** _Do you have a reservation?_

B Yes, we do. **2**_____?

A Of course. What's the name, please?

B It's Sarilaksana.

A Here it is: Mr and Mrs Sarilaksana. **3**_____?

B Sure. One question: **4**_____?

A Yes, there's a connection in all of the rooms. I'll give you a code and you have to write it on your electronic device.

B **5**_____?

A That's your mobile phone, tablet or laptop computer.

B Thank you.

Body and mind

9.1 The rise and fall of the handshake

Vocabulary body and actions

1 Match verbs 1–10 to definitions a–j.

1	bump	a	push something with a part of your body
2	clap	b	move your mouth to show that you are happy
3	hug	c	show part of your body
4	kiss	d	touch somebody with your lips
5	nod	e	hit a part of your body against something
6	press	f	move quickly from side to side or up and down
7	shake	g	move your head up and down
8	smile	h	put your arms around somebody
9	stick out	i	put your hand or finger on somebody
10	touch	j	hit your hands together

2 Label the photo with the parts of the body in the box.

> cheek chest chin elbow ~~forehead~~ lip shoulder thumb

1 forehead
2
3
5
6
4
7
8

3 Complete the article with the words in the box.

> cheek elbows ~~fist~~ hug nod shake smile touch

Body language around the world

When you are abroad, you must be careful how you express yourself with your body. If you make your hand into a ¹ _fist_ and begin to shake it at somebody, most people will understand that you're angry. But not all actions mean the same in every country.

In Asia, people are very careful not to ² _____ anybody with their foot. And, like many other countries, they never put their feet on chairs and tables where they are sitting.

In Fiji, people ³ _____ hands for a very long time. Don't worry if this continues for all of your conversation – it's normal.

Greetings in some European countries are often quite physical. People kiss friends and family on the ⁴ _____, and they often ⁵ _____.

In countries like France, what you do at the dinner table is very important. Don't put your ⁶ _____ on the table, and don't eat with your fingers. People will think you are rude if you do this.

Some countries have different ways of saying 'yes' and 'no'. In Greece and Bulgaria, people shake their head for yes and ⁷ _____ for no. This can be confusing, so it's probably better to learn the words for yes and no.

However, there is one international expression that everybody understands. If you are having problems and you don't know what to say, the best thing to do is ⁸ _____.

Grammar *if* + present simple, *will/won't/ might*

4 Match the two halves of the sentences.

1 They'll think you're rude   a you might miss the traffic.
2 Will he be angry   b I won't remember it.
3 If you leave now,   c if I don't shake his hand?
4 Everything will be fine   d it won't be the end of the world.
5 If you make a mistake,   e I might help you.
6 Will you translate for me   f if you don't say *hello*.
7 If you ask me nicely,   g if you smile a lot.
8 If I don't write it down   h if I don't understand them?

Learning a language effectively

5 Choose the correct option to complete the sentences.

1 If you *tell* / *'ll tell* me your secret, I *don't say* / *won't say* anything.
2 I *call* / *'ll call* you if I *get* / *'ll get* lost.
3 *Do you come* / *Will you come* to my wedding if I *invite* / *'ll invite* you?
4 If we *don't get up* / *won't get up* early, we *don't have* / *won't have* enough time.
5 I *get* / *might get* a taxi if we *finish* / *'ll finish* late.
6 *Do you enjoy* / *Will you enjoy* the holiday, if your partner *doesn't go* / *won't go*?
7 If you *don't speak* / *won't speak* the language, you *get* / *might get* bored.
8 It *is* / *'ll be* cheaper if we *go* / *'ll go* by bus.

PRONUNCIATION *'ll*

6a **9.1**))) Listen to the pronunciation of *'ll*.

b **9.1**))) Listen again. Pause the CD and repeat after each short form.

7 Complete the text with the correct form of the verbs in brackets.

One of the best ways of learning a language is to spend some time in a country where people speak the language. If you ¹ _go_ (go) to Moscow, for example, you ² _____ (learn) Russian a lot more quickly than if you stay at home going to classes twice a week. It is probably better to go on this trip alone. If you ³ _____ (travel) in a group, you ⁴ _____ (spend) all your time speaking your own language with your friends.

Another option is to try and find a job abroad. If you ⁵ _____ (work) in a restaurant in Paris, for example, you ⁶ _____ (have to) speak French to the customers all day. Another idea is to share a flat with some people from the country. If you ⁷ _____ (find) a room in a shared flat in Berlin, for example, your German ⁸ _____ (be) fantastic by the time you go home. You could also try living with a family and looking after their children while you're away. The only problem is that you ⁹ _____ (feel) lonely if you ¹⁰ _____ (not go) out) much. You ¹¹ _____ (not meet) anybody if you ¹² _____ (stay) in your room all day, so it's important to find somebody to talk to. If you ¹³ _____ (practise) the language a lot, you ¹⁴ _____ (feel) much more confident. Spending time abroad is a great experience, and you might not want to come home at the end of it!

I can ...	Very well	Quite well	More practice
talk about greetings.	○	○	○
talk about possible situations and the results.	○	○	○

9.2 Going back to nature

Vocabulary health and fitness

1   Complete the puzzle with words for health and fitness.

```
1 W E I G H T L I F T I N G
          2 F I T N E S S
```

(crossword grid with:)
1 WEIGHTLIFTING
2 FITNESS (down)

1   a sport in which people have to be very strong
2   small living things that can make you ill
3   always busy and doing a lot of things
4   a very dangerous illness
5   the food that you usually eat
6   serious illnesses
7   a feeling of worry because of problems in your life

2   Complete the words in the sentences.

1   Some people _relax_ by reading or watching TV.
2   Crisps, burgers and pizzas are kinds of j_____
    f_____.
3   Bad news can sometimes make you feel d_____.
4   Walking and swimming are kinds of g_____
    e_____.
5   Colds and flu are different kinds of i_____.
6   F_____ is about being healthy and strong.
7   Meat, vegetables and fruit are kinds of n_____
    f_____.
8   C_____ is a sport that you do with a bike.

3   Complete the text with the words in the box.

active   cancer   depressed   diet   diseases
fitness   junk food   ~~natural food~~

Seven-a-day

Many world governments today have realized the importance of eating **1** _natural food_ and so they are recommending that people eat seven pieces of fruit and vegetables a day. They say that this will protect the body from dangerous **2**_____, especially of the heart, and it may also stop people from getting illnesses such as **3**_____. Doctors have said that we need to look carefully at our **4**_____ if we want to stay healthy. They say that eating too much **5**_____ can make people fat, but it can also make them feel **6**_____. The wrong food can have a very negative effect on our mental health. People who eat healthily are generally more **7**_____ than those who do not, because they have more energy to do sport. The idea is that if we take our health and **8**_____ seriously by eating the right food and by doing the right exercise, we will be much happier when we are older and we will live longer.

PRONUNCIATION *eat* and *bread*

4a   Look at the pairs of words. Put a tick (✓) if the pronunciation of *ea* is the same in each pair and put a cross (✗) if it is different.

1 eat	read	✓
2 bread	meat	✗
3 disease	dream	___
4 easy	weather	___
5 health	leather	___
6 already	instead	___
7 breakfast	team	___
8 cleaner	pleased	___

b   **9.2**)) Listen and check.

c   **9.2**)) Listen again. Pause the CD and repeat after each word.

Grammar present tenses in future time clauses

5 Choose the correct option to complete the sentences.

1 They'll be really pleased *before* / *if* / (*when*) they hear your good news.

2 You won't get the job *after* / *if* / *when* you don't speak good English.

3 He'll look for a new job *after* / *before* / *if* he comes back from his holiday.

4 She'll stay in bed again *as soon as* / *if* / *when* she doesn't feel better tomorrow.

5 We won't have time for breakfast *as soon as* / *before* / *if* we leave.

6 I'll call you *as soon as* / *before* / *if* I arrive at my hotel.

6 Use the words to write sentences about the future.

1 you / be late / if / you / not hurry up
   You'll be late if you don't hurry up.

2 I / call you / as soon as / I / get my results
   _____

3 we / be disappointed / if / our daughter / not go to university
   _____

4 they / go travelling / after / they / finish their course
   _____

5 she / talk to her boss / before / she / make a decision
   _____

6 we / not go to the party / if / we / not be invited
   _____

7 my son / learn to drive / when / he / be 18
   _____

8 you / not get better / if / you / not practise
   _____

7 Complete the leaflet with the correct form of the verbs in the box.

finish   go   not have   not like   see   start   tell   ~~want~~

Change your life with yoga

Yoga is a great way to relax if you're feeling stressed, so why not try a class near you? Visit some of the studios in your area and choose the one which you like best. The teacher **1** _will want_ to talk to you when you sign up for a class. He or she will ask you some questions about your general health and fitness before you **2**_____ for the first time. Find out if the studio has equipment. You might have to take your own if the studio **3**_____ any. On the first day, the instructor **4**_____ you where to stand when you enter the studio. Studios have their own rules, but you will probably need to turn off your mobile phone before the class **5**_____. Listen to the instructor and watch what the others are doing. The instructor will only come and help you if he or she **6**_____ that you are having problems. The first class is usually free and you won't have to go back if you **7**_____ it. But most people love yoga. You'll feel very relaxed after the class **8**_____. All you need to do then is to go home, have a nice hot shower and change into some comfortable clothes for the rest of the day.

I can ...	Very well	Quite well	More practice
talk about health and fitness.	○	○	○
use present tenses in future time clauses.	○	○	○

9.3 Vocabulary development

verbs and prepositions

→ **STUDY TIP** Have a separate page in your vocabulary notebook for each preposition. Draw a mind map on the page. Every time you come across a verb which takes one of the prepositions, write it in the correct section. This will make it easier for you to remember which preposition to use.

1 Choose the correct option to complete the sentences.
1 My partner works (for)/ on / to a multinational company.
2 I've always dreamed of / in / on having a big house by the sea.
3 We might go camping at the weekend, but it depends of / in / on the weather.
4 Can you think in / of / on somewhere nice to have dinner tonight?
5 Did you succeed in / of / on passing all your exams?
6 This jacket doesn't belong for / of / to me. Is it yours?

2 Complete the conversations with the correct form of the verbs in the box with the prepositions *for, in, of, on* or *to*.

not believe   belong   consist   depend   succeed   think
work

1 **A** Is this your apartment?

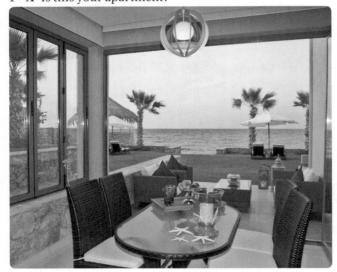

B No, it _belongs to_ my parents. They let me use it in the summer.
2 **A** What does your partner do?
B She's a lawyer. She _____ _____ an international law firm.
3 **A** What shall we get your mother for her birthday?

B I don't know. I can't _____ _____ anything.
4 **A** Do you think there is life on other planets?
B No, I _____ _____ _____ aliens.
5 **A** What time will we arrive?
B I'm not sure. It _____ _____ the traffic.
6 **A** What's Spanish omelette?
B It's a dish that _____ _____ eggs and potatoes.
7 **A** Why are you so happy?
B I finally _____ _____ getting a job.

Vocabulary review

3 Complete the table with the body and action words in the box.

chest   ~~clap~~   elbow   forehead   hug   nod   shake
shoulder   touch   tongue

actions	body
1 _clap_	6 _____
2 _____	7 _____
3 _____	8 _____
4 _____	9 _____
5 _____	10 _____

4 Complete the missing vowels in the health and fitness words.
being ill [1] c_a_nc_e_r, diseases, [2] _lln_ss_s, viruses
doing / not doing exercise [3] _ct_v_, cycling, [4] f_tn_ss, gentle exercise, [5] r_l_x, weightlifting
eating [6] d_ _t, junk food, [7] n_t_r_l f_ _d
mental health [8] d_pr_ss_d, stress

5 Complete the verbs with the prepositions in the box.

for   in   of   on   ~~to~~

belong [1] _to_   succeed [7] _____
believe [2] _____ think [8] _____
consist [3] _____ work [9] _____
depend [4] _____
dream [5] _____
happen [6] _____

9.4 Speaking and writing

Speaking asking for help and giving advice

1 Put the conversation in the correct order 1–8.

_1_ Hello. Please have a seat. Now, what can I do for you?

___ It's one tablet with meals three times a day. And you mustn't do any sport for a week.

___ Right. Thanks very much for your help.

___ Let me have a look. It isn't broken, but I don't think you should walk on it.

___ Yes, it hurts a lot. Could you give me something for the pain?

___ OK. How often should I take the tablets?

___ I've hurt my foot. I was playing football and I fell over.

___ Yes, I'll give you some painkillers. You could try putting ice on your foot, too.

2a Complete the conversation with the phrases in the box.

| It's a good idea | ~~How can I help you?~~ | I think you should |
| Have you got anything | you could try | You mustn't |

A Morning. ¹ _How can I help you?_

B Hello. ² _____ for a cold?

A Well, there isn't much I can do really.
³ _____ go home and get lots of rest.

B Can you give me something for my cough? It's very annoying.

A Yes, ⁴ _____ this medicine. Take it every six hours until the cough goes away.

B Right.

A ⁵ _____ to drink lots of water, too. And keep warm. ⁶ _____ go out.

B OK. Thank you very much.

b 9.3))) Listen and check your answers.

Writing a formal covering letter

3 Complete the letters with the words in the box.

| additional | ~~Dear~~ | details | enclose | enclosed | faithfully |
| hear | hearing | like | Madam | sincerely | wish |

---

¹ _Dear_ Mr Thompson

I ² _____ to apply for your MovNat course in the first week of June.

As requested, I ³ _____ my completed application form in English and a current medical certificate.

Please contact me if you require any ⁴ _____ information.

I hope to ⁵ _____ from you soon.

Yours ⁶ _____

Jens Schmidt

Dear Sir / ⁷ _____

I would ⁸ _____ to request a refund for the T-shirt that I purchased from your company.

Please find ⁹ _____ the T-shirt and my completed returns form.

Please inform me if you require any further ¹⁰ _____.

I look forward to ¹¹ _____ from you.

Yours ¹² _____

Mitsuki Akimoto

I can …	Very well	Quite well	More practice
use verbs and prepositions.	○	○	○
ask for help and give advice.	○	○	○
write a formal covering letter.	○	○	○

10 Food

10.1 A question of taste

Vocabulary describing food

1 Complete the crossword from the clues below.

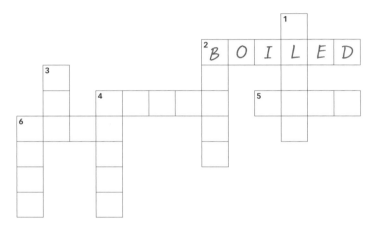

Across ▶
2 cooked in water heated to 100°C
4 food that you eat quickly between main meals
5 not having a strong taste
6 a dish made by cooking meat and vegetables in liquid for a long time

Down ▼
1 simple, not complicated
2 cooked in an oven on a dry heat
3 causing a burning feeling in your mouth
4 tastes as if it contains a lot of sugar
6 having a sharp taste like a lemon

2 Complete the descriptions and match sentences 1–4 to photos a–d.

1 We have this as a light m_eal_ . It's m_____ with rice and it has r_____ fish in it. Photo ___
2 It's a s_____ of pie, but it's _____, not sweet. It's made with eggs and small pieces of bacon. You can e_____ it hot or cold. Photo ___
3 It has cooked meat or vegetables and sp_____ in it. It t_____ quite hot. It's often s_____ with rice. Photo ___
4 It's a k_____ of dessert. It's made with some special cakes, but it has a b_____ taste because it h_____ coffee in it. Photo ___

3 Complete the menu with the words in the box.

dessert   fried   ~~herbs~~   honey   lamb   sauce   spicy   thick

Rosie's Kitchen

Starter
Potato soup with fresh **1** _herbs_
2 _____ prawns – quite hot!

Main course
Boiled ham with cheese **3**_____ and carrots
4_____ fish with chips and peas
Roast **5**_____ with roast potatoes and mixed vegetables

6_____
Apple pie with **7**_____ double cream
Greek yoghurt with **8**_____

PRONUNCIATION number of syllables in words

4a Complete the table with the words in the box.

~~chocolate~~ different favourite interesting raspberry restaurant several strawberry temperature vegetable

Two-syllable words	Three-syllable words
chocolate	_____
_____	_____
_____	
_____	
_____	

b **10.1**))) Listen and check.

c **10.1**))) Listen again. Pause the CD and repeat after each word.

Grammar uses of the -ing form

5 Match the two halves of the sentences.

1 We're really looking forward to _b_
2 Is your boyfriend interested in ___
3 They ended the meal by ___
4 I really don't mind ___
5 Do you enjoy ___
6 The children haven't finished ___

a learning how to cook?
b giving our first dinner party.
c doing the washing up.
d eating their soup.
e ordering some coffee.
f going to concerts?

➔ **STUDY TIP** Make a note of any irregular -ing forms in your notebook, e.g. write – writing, stop – stopping. This will make it easier for you to remember the correct spelling.

6 Complete the sentences with the -ing form of the verbs in brackets. Then write **V** if the -ing form is after a verb, **P** after a preposition and **S** if it is used as a subject.

1 I hate _buying_ food at the weekend. The supermarket is always full. (buy) _V_
2 _____ a large meal can make you feel sleepy. (have) ___
3 This dessert is delicious! I could go on _____ it forever. (eat) ___
4 We get most of our vegetables by _____ our own food. (grow) ___
5 I don't feel like _____ tonight. Let's go out for dinner. (cook) ___
6 _____ eight glasses of water a day is good for your health. (drink) ___
7 I always buy birthday cakes because I'm not very good at _____ them. (make) ___
8 _____ food in the microwave is quicker than putting it in the oven. (heat) ___
9 Kate is worried about _____ her husband's family for a meal. (invite) ___

7 Complete the article with the -ing form of the verbs in the box.

eat finish get ~~go~~ know prepare serve tell try

The very best food

What do you think about ¹ _going_ to Michelin-starred restaurants? It is only the very best restaurants that have a Michelin star, but you can find them all over the world. It is true that they are more expensive than usual and the bill often comes to hundreds of pounds, but foodies love ² _____ at these restaurants. ³ _____ the dishes is often a wonderful experience because the chefs have spent hours ⁴ _____ each one of them. There are usually a lot of chefs in the kitchen, and each one is responsible for one of the dishes on the menu.

⁵ _____ a Michelin star is a great honour for a restaurant, because it means that the head chef is one of the best in the profession. Michelin inspectors visit restaurants without ⁶ _____ anybody that they are coming, so that the chefs cannot make any special preparations. But usually, the chef has an idea that an inspector is in the area because a chef from another restaurant tells him or her. After ⁷ _____ their meal, the inspector pays the bill and leaves, like all the other customers. It is only later that the chef finds out his or her opinion of the restaurant. ⁸ _____ that perhaps they are cooking for a Michelin inspector can make chefs very nervous. They usually prefer ⁹ _____ normal customers, who do not have to make such an important decision about the food.

I can …	Very well	Quite well	More practice
describe a national dish.	○	○	○
use the -ing form.	○	○	○

10.2 Canned dreams

1 Find eight food and drink containers in the word search.

B	O	C	A	B	O	X	T	K	T
O	P	J	A	O	C	K	E	L	A
C	C	A	R	T	O	N	B	O	S
R	J	R	E	T	U	B	E	R	O
O	C	T	R	L	I	N	J	N	R
P	A	C	K	E	T	F	C	B	X
D	N	T	I	R	I	B	U	F	U
C	A	J	A	T	N	R	S	T	P

2a Complete the shopping list for a summer party.

Kim's party

four ¹ _tins_ (SINT) of chicken soup

six ² _____ (STACKEP) of sausages

two ³ _____ (OLSBETT) of ketchup

two ⁴ _____ (UBSET) of tomato paste

three ⁵ _____ (SARJ) of olives

two ⁶ _____ (XEBOS) of strawberries

four ⁷ _____ (SARCONT) of cream

sixteen ⁸ _____ (SCNA) of drinks

b **10.2**))) Listen and check.

c **10.2**))) Listen and repeat the phrases in exercise **2a**.

3 Complete the article with the words in exercise **1**.

Space food

Eating in space is much more difficult than it is on Earth because food does not stay in one place. Astronauts can only have 1.7 kilograms of food per person per day, so the size and weight of the container is important. You won't find a ¹ _jar_ of jam or a glass ² _____ of water on the International Space Station because glass is too heavy. You won't see a ³ _____ of apples either, because fresh fruit doesn't last very long.

In the past, all of the food in space had the same texture as toothpaste, and astronauts had a ⁴ _____ of food at each meal. Now things have changed and most of the containers are made of plastic. However, some food is the same as it is at home, and perhaps once a week, it is possible to have a ⁵ _____ of tuna or a ⁶ _____ of ham for lunch.

Drinking is also more difficult in space. Most drinks come in plastic cups, and astronauts have to add cold or hot water to the cup. You won't find a ⁷ _____ of lemonade or a ⁸ _____ of juice anywhere in space.

Grammar the passive

4 Choose the correct option to complete the sentences.
1 Most people in China (drink) / *is drunk* tea.
2 The chef *didn't cook* / *weren't cooked* the potatoes enough.
3 The pizzas *delivered* / *were delivered* to our house.
4 We *ate* / *were eaten* sushi for lunch yesterday.
5 Cans *don't make* / *aren't made* of plastic.
6 Hamburgers *didn't invent* / *weren't invented* in the USA.
7 You *don't use* / *aren't used* pasta to make paella.
8 Coffee *produces* / *is produced* in Brazil.

5 Use the words to write present or past passive sentences.
1 eggs / pack / in boxes of six or twelve
   Eggs are packed in boxes of six or twelve.
2 rice / not grow / in cold places
   _____
3 this bread / bake / yesterday
   _____
4 meals / not eat / in front of the TV when I was young
   _____
5 milk / not sell / in cartons in the past
   _____
6 toast / make / with bread
   _____
7 those apple trees / plant / last year
   _____
8 olives / not usually serve / for dessert
   _____

6 Complete the article with the correct passive form of the verbs in brackets.

Pizza: the world's favourite dish

Millions of pizzas **1** _are eaten_ (eat) every day, but have you ever wondered where the pizza came from? In the 16th century, a kind of flat bread called 'pizza' **2**_____ (sell) on the streets of Naples. The bread was very plain and it **3**_____ (not buy) by many people, only the poor. Ingredients **4**_____ (not add) to this pizza until the middle of the 19th century, when the pizza became more popular. A few years later, one of the city's pizza makers tried out a new idea on the king's wife, Margherita of Savoy. He made a pizza with mozzarella cheese, tomatoes and herbs on top, and the queen loved it! The man's name was Raffaele Esposito and his experiment became known as the Pizza Margherita. Today, this pizza is typical in Naples, but only if it **5**_____ (prepare) by hand. There are a lot of rules telling chefs how to make traditional pizzas and machines **6**_____ (not use). Pizza makers have to use a special oven, too.

Pizzas **7**_____ (take) to other countries at the end of the 19th century by Italian immigrants looking for work. Some immigrants made pizzas at home to sell on the streets, while others opened pizzerias. Today, the pizza **8**_____ (not only serve) to customers in restaurants; people can call a restaurant to order a pizza to eat at home.

I can ...	Very well	Quite well	More practice
talk about food.	○	○	○
use the passive.	○	○	○

10.3 Vocabulary development

words with more than one meaning

Vocabulary review

1 Read the text and choose the correct meaning (*a* or *b*) for the words in *italics*.

> Do you know what a freegan is? It's a person who has found a completely new ¹ *way* of feeding their family. Freegans are against the high ² *figures* of wasted food in our society and so they are trying to do something about it. A freegan's ³ *diet* is made up of things that other people throw away. They find most of their food in the bins outside large supermarkets. Freegans often go there to wait for the products that are ⁴ *left* at the end of the day. They can often find vegetables with a few ⁵ *marks* or fruit that is a ⁶ *funny* shape. Supermarkets do not ⁷ *charge* freegans for the food they take, so all of their meals are completely free. And most of the products are safe because they aren't usually ⁸ *past* their sell-by date.

1 a distance ⓑ method
2 a the shape of human bodies b numbers
3 a food they normally eat b food they eat to get thinner
4 a remaining, still there b opposite of right
5 a spots that spoil something b scores of a test or essay
6 a making you laugh b strange
7 a ask them to pay a price b put electricity into a battery
8 a later than b the time before now

2 Complete the sentences with five of the words in exercise **1**. Use the same word for each pair of sentences.

1 **A** Do you eat a healthy _____?
   B The doctor has told me to go on a _____.

2 **A** Throw that orange away. It looks a bit _____.
   B The waiter was really _____. He made us laugh.

3 **A** In the _____, this café used to be very popular.
   B Do you ever eat yoghurts that are _____ their sell-by date?

4 **A** The eggs are at the back of the shop on the _____.
   B It's nearly closing time, so there isn't any bread _____.

5 **A** There's a strange _____ on that apple. Don't eat it.
   B What _____ would you give the meal – a seven?

Vocabulary review

3 Complete the missing vowels in the food words.

how it is eaten	¹ b<u>a</u>ked, boiled, ² fr__d, raw
ingredients	herbs, ³ h_n_y, lamb, ⁴ sp_c_s
taste and texture	⁵ b_tt_r, hot/spicy, ⁶ m_ld, plain, ⁷ s_v__ry, sour, ⁸ sw__t, thick
type of dish	dessert, ⁹ s__ce, snack, ¹⁰st_w

4 Match the two halves of the sentences.

1 It's a kind / sort of   a the summer.
2 It's made with   b delicious.
3 It has   c a starter.
4 People have this as   d soup.
5 You can eat it in   e garlic in it
6 It has a sour   f tomatoes and other vegetables.
7 It's often served   g taste.
8 It tastes   h with small pieces of tomato and onion.

5 Complete the phrases with the words in the box.

> ~~bottle~~ box can carton jar packet tin tube

a ¹ *bottle* of lemonade, vinegar, water
a ² _____ of tomato paste, toothpaste
a ³ _____ of cereal, chocolates, eggs
a ⁴ _____ of baby food, jam, olives
a ⁵ _____ of energy drink, fruit juice, lemonade
a ⁶ _____ of carrots, tomatoes, tuna
a ⁷ _____ of juice, milk, soup
a ⁸ _____ of crisps, frozen peas, rice

6 Complete the words.

1 ch<u>arge</u>   ask a price / put electricity into a battery
2 cl_____   obvious / something that you can see through
3 d_____   food you normally eat / food you eat to get thinner
4 f_____   a number / the shape of the human body
5 f_____   making you laugh / strange
6 l_____   opposite of right / remaining, still there
7 m_____   a spot that spoils the look of something / a score in a test or essay
8 p_____   later than / the time before now

10.4 Speaking and writing

Speaking problems in a restaurant

1 Choose the correct phrase, *a*, *b* or *c*.

What do you say if …

1 there's a problem with your order?
   a I do apologize.
   (b) There seems to be a mistake.
   c Don't worry about it.

2 you want the waiter to give you something?
   a Would you mind bringing me another one?
   b It's not your fault.
   c You've charged us for two, but we've only had one.

3 you want to make an apology?
   a I'm afraid it's wrong.
   b Could you possibly change it?
   c I'm terribly sorry.

2a Decide if the conversations belong to Conversation 1 or Conversation 2. Write *1* or *2*.

   _1_ **Customer (C)** Excuse me? I'm afraid I can't eat this steak. It's raw.
   _2_ **C** Excuse me? Could you possibly bring me the bill?
   ___ **Waiter (W)** Yes, of course … Here it is.
   ___ **W** Really? I'll take it back to the kitchen for you.
   ___ **C** No, I'd like to order something else, please.
   ___ **C** Oh. There seems to be a mistake.
   ___ **W** Is there?
   ___ **W** Of course. What would you like?
   ___ **C** Yes. You've charged me for the steak, but I didn't eat it.
   ___ **C** I'm not sure. Would you mind bringing me the menu again?
   ___ **W** You're absolutely right. I do apologize.
   ___ **W** Of course not. I'm terribly sorry about your steak.
   ___ **C** Don't worry about it. Erm, I'll have a salad, please.
   ___ **C** Don't worry. It's not your fault.

b **10.3**))) Listen and check.

Writing a restaurant review

3 Tick (✓) the sentences where the apostrophe is used correctly and put a cross (✗) if it is wrong. Correct the incorrect sentences.

1 It's a great restaurant.   ✓
2 It hasnt been open for long.   ✗
   It hasn't been open for long.
3 The owners' wife greeted us at the door.   ___
4 The waiter's were all very friendly.   ___
5 The other diners' meals looked delicious.   ___
6 My friend's and I will definitely go back.   ___
7 They haven't changed the menu.   ___
8 Hes forgotten the drinks.   ___

4 Complete the review with the words in the box.

| atmosphere | food | ~~location~~ | service | value for money |

 L A T E R A L

I took my boyfriend to Lateral for his birthday yesterday, and we weren't disappointed. The ¹ _location_ of the restaurant is not ideal as it's in a very narrow street where it's difficult to park. But the place was busy and it had a very lively ² _____, so we didn't mind. The ³ _____ was excellent and the waiters and waitresses were all very helpful. But the best thing about the restaurant was the ⁴ _____. My prawns were delicious, and the vegetables were cooked perfectly. My boyfriend's fish was delicious too. I had a nice surprise when I asked for the bill as the price was very reasonable. We both thought the meal was fantastic ⁵ _____. We've already told all our friends about Lateral because we had such a good time.

I can …	Very well	Quite well	More practice
understand words with more than one meaning.	○	○	○
explain and deal with problems.	○	○	○
write a review of a restaurant.	○	○	○

10.5 Reading for pleasure

Making chocolate

1   Look at the photo of a cacao pod. Match words 1–4 to definitions a–d.

1	pod	a	the soft inside part of a pod
2	shell	b	the fruit of the cacao tree
3	pulp	c	the seeds of the cacao tree
4	beans	d	the hard outside part of a pod

2   Read an extract from a factfile.

3   Complete the summary.

> Cacao ¹ *pods* begin to grow when a tree is about
> ² _____ years old. When the pods change
> ³ _____, people take them down and cut
> them open. First they put the cacao beans in large
> ⁴ _____ covered with ⁵ _____ leaves for up to
> a week. Then they dry the beans on large ⁶ _____
> in the sun for two or three weeks. After that, the
> farmers sell the beans to ⁷ _____, who sell them
> on to ⁸ _____ to be made into chocolate bars.

4   Think about the process of making chocolate. Did you know before how chocolate was made?
    Do you like chocolate? Why/Why not? If so, which type of chocolate is your favourite?

From cacao pod to chocolate bar

The cacao tree begins to have its first pods after about three years. It is very different from most other trees because its flowers and then its pods grow from the centre of the tree.

The large cacao pods are wonderful to see. At first, they are a beautiful light green. But after six months, when they are ready to open, they become very colourful. They can be bright red or orange, dark purple or deep green.

The people on the plantation take down the pods with very long sticks. Then they cut them open with big knives. Inside they find between 20 and 40 cacao beans in the soft white pulp. The beans are very hard and they do not smell or taste like chocolate.

The workers then usually put the beans and the pulp in large boxes with some banana leaves on the top. They leave these in the hot sun for four to seven days and some of the chemicals in the beans begin to change.

The beans are now very different. They are no longer white or purple – they are dark brown. And very importantly, they smell of wonderful chocolate!

Next, the plantation workers put the beans onto large tables. They dry the beans in the sun for ten to twenty days and move them from time to time. On larger plantations they dry them in special buildings. But the best chocolate comes from beans which stay in the sun for a long time.

The farmers then put the beans into bags of about 64 kilograms each and sell them to brokers – business people who buy and sell cacao beans for money. The brokers then sell them to the chocolate factories. But the chocolate factories do not just buy one type of bean. Beans from different countries, or even from different factories, taste different. In the factories, people mix together different types of bean to get chocolate with just the right taste.

Text extract from *Oxford Bookworms Factfiles: Chocolate*

Review: Units 9 and 10

Grammar

1 Choose the correct option to complete the sentences.

1 Paella *is made* / *makes* / *is making* with rice.
2 The children *have* / *having* / *will have* a snack later if they get hungry.
3 We avoid *buy* / *buying* / *will buy* white bread because it's unhealthy.
4 We'll have dinner as soon as it *'ll be* / *'s* / *was* ready.
5 If it *doesn't rain* / *don't rain* / *won't rain*, we'll have a barbecue this weekend.
6 I'm going to give up *eat* / *eating* / *will eat* biscuits.
7 Before I *start* / *starting* / *will start* cooking today's lunch, I'll get changed.
8 Potatoes *are taking* / *took* / *were taken* to Europe in the sixteenth century.

2 Complete the text with the correct form of the verbs in brackets.

> **1** *Growing* (grow) your own food does not have to be difficult, say the people of Todmorden. If you visit this town in the north of England, you **2**_____ (not see) many people in the shops. This is because most of the residents prefer **3**_____ (eat) the food they grow. Todmorden is part of the 'Incredible Edible' project, which **4**_____ (start) by two women who live in the town. The group believes that if they **5**_____ (not prepare) for the future, there won't be enough food for everybody. Fruit and vegetables **6**_____ (plant) everywhere, there are even some lettuces outside the police station. But people grow things without **7**_____ (expect) anybody to pay for them. When food **8**_____ (begin) to disappear from the shops in the future, the people of Todmorden know they will be safe.

Vocabulary

3 Circle the word that is different.

1 clap   fist   kiss   nod
2 boiled   baked   depressed   fried
3 diseases herbs   illnesses   viruses
4 cycling   fitness   forehead   weightlifting
5 active   bitter   sour   sweet
6 hug   greet   touch   tongue
7 box   dessert   jar   packet
8 elbow   shoulder stress   thumb

4 Complete the text with the missing words.

> Goulash is one of the national dishes of Hungary, but it is also popular in Central and Southern Europe and Scandinavia. It's a **1** s*avoury* dish, which is a main meal. Goulash is a kind of **2** st_____ which is made with meat, such as beef or **3** l_____ and vegetables. It tastes quite **4** sp_____, because it has paprika in it. Different varieties of goulash can be made by adding a **5** c_____ of sour cream or a **6** t_____ of beans. In some countries, part of a **7** b_____ of tomato sauce or a **8** t_____ of tomato paste may also be used to make the goulash thicker.

5 Complete the sentences with the words in the box.

> diet funny in left ~~mark~~ of on to

1 I don't want that apple – it has a _mark_ on it.
2 Can you think _____ a nice restaurant where we can have dinner tonight?
3 I think I need to go on a _____ because my clothes feel uncomfortable.
4 We might have lunch in the garden, but it depends _____ the weather.
5 I don't believe _____ taking tablets to lose weight.
6 Throw that milk away if it tastes _____.
7 Can you get some eggs if you happen _____ remember?
8 I can't make you a sandwich because there isn't any bread _____.

Speaking

6 Put the words in the correct order to make sentences.

1 you / bed / should / I / in / think / stay
   I think you should stay in bed.
2 me / clean / possibly / you / plate / give / Could / a
   _____
3 heavy / mustn't / anything / You / lift
   _____
4 a / seems / the / There / in / be / bill / to / mistake
   _____
5 a / Have / throat / anything / you / for / got / sore
   _____
6 on / try / You / some / could / it / cream / putting
   _____

11 World

11.1 Making the world a better place

Vocabulary global issues

1 Match words 1–9 to definitions a–i.

1	advance	a	the state of somebody's body or mind
2	environment	b	putting scientific discoveries into practice
3	farming	c	the study of natural laws and the physical world
4	health	d	the state of being healthy and happy
5	population	e	something new in a particular field
6	science	f	the natural world around us
7	technology	g	the number of people that live in a place
8	unemployment	h	the number of people who cannot find a job
9	well-being	i	growing food and looking after animals

2 Choose the correct option to complete the sentences.

1 Minis are made in a *shop / factory* in Oxford.
2 The new shopping centre will *create / spread* new jobs in the area.
3 The weather is changing because of *world / global* warming.
4 You can read about the facts and *numbers / figures* in the latest report.
5 Do you agree that money brings *happiness / happy*?
6 Scientists are hoping to find a *cure / treat* for cancer soon.
7 People have less money since the start of the financial *crisis / problem*.
8 Illnesses like flu *create / spread* very quickly.
9 World *hunger / hungry* affects many countries, especially those in Africa.

3 Complete the article with the words in the box.

environment factories facts financial ~~global~~ health
hunger situation unemployment warming

Cutting down on world pollution

The countries of the world sometimes meet to discuss ¹ _global_ issues. Two of the most important meetings were the *Earth Summit* in Rio de Janeiro in 1992 and *Rio +20* in the same city in 2012. At the meetings, world leaders talked about different ways they could protect the ² _____. They looked at all the ³ _____ and figures from industry in different countries and agreed that ⁴ _____ shouldn't produce so much pollution. They hoped that this would slow down global ⁵ _____. They also looked at pollution from cars on the streets, which they say is bad for people's ⁶ _____. At the meeting, they recommended that cities should have more public transport, and people should stop using their cars. Some people think that governments should do more about the world's problems. They say that there is enough food for everybody, so world ⁷ _____ should not exist. Unfortunately, most people are worried about the economic ⁸ _____ in their own countries today. In many places, companies have closed because of the ⁹ _____ crisis, so many workers have lost their jobs. Today, ¹⁰ _____ is a problem in many countries, and it is a difficult one to solve.

Grammar *if* + past tense + *would*

4a Put the words in the correct order to make sentences and questions.

1 a / I / work / would / I / car, / had / If / drive / to
   If _I had a car, I would drive to work._

2 be / job / wouldn't / I / my / if / I / happy / lost
   I _____.

3 time / you / What / in / go / if / do / could / you / back / would
   What _____?

4 she / him / his / knew / she'd / phone number, / If / call
   If _____.

5 you / if / choice / you / live / would / Where / the / had
   Where _____?

6 exercise / better / did / if / feel / you / 'd / some
   You _____.

PRONUNCIATION *if* + past tense + *would* sentences

b **11.1**))) Listen to sentence 1 in exercise **4a**. Notice how the stressed words are <u>underlined</u> and the intonation is marked in the sentence.

If I had a <u>car</u>, I would <u>drive</u> to <u>work</u>.

c **11.2**))) Listen to sentences 2–6 in exercise **4a**. <u>Underline</u> the stressed words and mark the intonation in the sentences.

d **11.2**))) Listen again. Pause the CD and repeat after each sentence.

---

5 Complete the sentences with the correct form of the verbs in brackets.

1 If you _worked_ less, you _would have_ more free time. (work, have)

2 People _____ the country if unemployment _____ so high. (not leave, not be)

3 Where _____ you _____ on holiday if you _____ a lot of money? (go, have)

4 You _____ tired if you _____ so early. (not be, not get up)

5 We _____ a dog if we _____ in the country. (have, live)

6 If it _____, plants _____. (not rain, not grow)

7 I _____ the weekend more if I _____ on Saturdays. (enjoy, not work)

8 What _____ you _____ if you _____ your country's leader? (say, meet)

6 Complete the article with the correct form of the verbs in the box.

be   become   not eat   go   ~~happen~~   not need

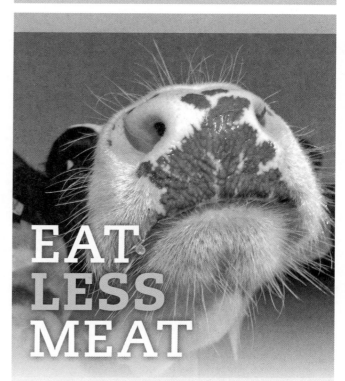

EAT LESS MEAT

What **1** _would happen_ if everybody in the world stopped eating meat? There is no question that humans eat far too much meat, but **2**_____ it really _____ better if all of us were vegetarians? Every day, millions of people around the world work with animals on farms. If we all **3**_____ vegetarians, there would be fewer animals to look after. We would keep cows to give us milk and hens to give us eggs, but we **4**_____ as many farm workers. Where **5**_____ they _____ to find a new job? On the other hand, cows produce 18% of the world's greenhouse gases, so if we **6**_____ beef, it would be better for the environment. There are arguments for the world becoming vegetarian and arguments against it. Probably the best solution is to eat less meat, but not to stop eating it altogether.

I can …	Very well	Quite well	More practice
talk about global issues.	○	○	○
talk about unlikely situations in the future.	○	○	○

11.2 Breaking news

Grammar _used to_

1a Use the words to make sentences with _used to, didn't use to_ or _Did ... use to?_

1 my brother / work in a bank +
   My brother used to work in a bank.

2 we / not have a garden –
   _____

3 my parents / live in a flat +
   _____

4 you / have long hair ?
   _____

5 I / not drink coffee –
   _____

6 your boyfriend / have a motorbike ?
   _____

7 I / wear glasses +
   _____

PRONUNCIATION _to_ in _used to_

b **11.3** ⟫ Listen and check. Pay attention to the weak pronunciation of _to_ /tə/ in _used to_.

c **11.3** ⟫ Listen again and repeat the sentences.

2 Tick (✓) the sentences that are correct and put a cross (✗) if they are wrong. Correct the incorrect sentences.

1 I used to live with friends, but now I have my own flat. ✓

2 We didn't used to do anything at weekends, but now we go walking.
   ✗ _We didn't use to do anything at weekends, but now we go walking._

3 What kind of music did you used to listen to when you were a teenager?
   _____

4 My parents used to be more active than they are now.
   _____

5 One day, we used to have a car accident.
   _____

6 They didn't used to eat fish, but now they prefer it to meat.
   _____

7 Our children not use to go out at night, but now they do.
   _____

3 Complete the article with the correct form of the verbs in the box. Use _used to, didn't use to_ or _Did ... use to?_

> be not happen look read sit not smile ~~watch~~ not work

¹ _Did_ you _use to watch_ the news on TV when you were little? News programmes ² _____ very different in the past. Women ³ _____ as newsreaders then, but now both men and women do the job. Newsreaders ⁴ _____ very smart in the past because they always wore suits. They were more serious than they are now, and they ⁵ _____ a lot. Today newsreaders are a lot friendlier, and they don't wear such formal clothes. The programmes are also more enjoyable now because they show reports from all over the world. This ⁶ _____ in early news programmes because there wasn't the technology to send images from one place to another. In the past, the same newsreader ⁷ _____ the same news stories several times a day. That was when families ⁸ _____ together to watch the news because they only had one television.

Vocabulary the news

4 Label the photo with the words in the box.

election flood forest fire ~~hurricane~~ robbery strike

1 hurricane

2 _____

3 _____

4 _____

5 _____

6 _____

5 Complete the words in the sentences.

1 You can read _articles_ in a newspaper or a magazine.
2 If you have a c_____, your car hits something and is damaged.
3 J_____ are people whose job it is to collect and write about news.
4 A n_____ d_____ is an event like a flood or a hurricane that causes a lot of damage.
5 If you r_____ a place, you arrive there.
6 If you r_____ something, you tell people exactly what you have seen or heard.
7 You can share information quickly and easily on the internet if you use s_____ m_____.
8 When things s_____, they affect a larger area or a bigger group of people.
9 If something is u_____ t_____ d_____, it has the most recent information.
10 If a magazine is published w_____, it appears every seven days.

6 Complete the article with the words in exercise 5.

The power of nature

One of the worst **1** _natural disasters_ the world has ever seen was the 2011 tsunami. It was caused by a massive earthquake under the sea off the coast of Japan. In some areas, the water travelled up to 10 km from the coast, which made it difficult for rescue workers to **2**_____ the victims. **3**_____ flew to the area as soon as possible to **4**_____ on the damage, but before they got there, the news appeared on **5**_____. Once the story was on the internet, it quickly **6**_____ all over the world. For days after the event, there were **7**_____ in all the main newspapers explaining what was happening. The biggest danger came from a nuclear power plant called Fukushima which was in the area. Everybody wanted to be **8**_____ with the situation in the power plant. The **9**_____ magazines published photos of the tsunami that showed the power of the sea. The water picked up trees, buildings and cars and took them far away. In some places, the piles of vehicles looked like a big car **10**_____. It is estimated that around 19,000 people lost their lives in the tsunami.

I can ...	Very well	Quite well	More practice
talk about past habits and situations.	○	○	○
talk about the news.	○	○	○

11.3 Vocabulary development

Vocabulary phrasal verbs

1 Rewrite the words in *italics* with the phrasal verbs in the box.

> find out   give up   grow up   put down   put on   set up
> ~~take up~~

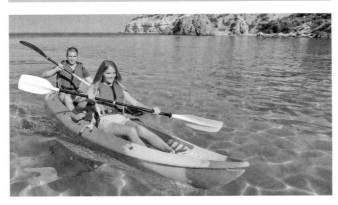

1 I've got more free time than I used to have, so I'm going to *start* a new sport. *take up*
2 We called the station to *discover* the times of the trains. _____
3 It was cold, so I *covered myself in* a warm coat before I left home. _____
4 People often ask children what they want to be when they *get older*. _____
5 They *placed* the new television carefully on the table. _____
6 I couldn't do the homework so in the end, I had to *stop*. _____
7 I know a lot about computers, but I can't afford to *start* my own company. _____

2 Rewrite the sentences using a pronoun instead of a noun.
1 When did you find out your results?
   When did you find them out?
2 I'm giving up eating sweets.
   _____
3 He put down his suitcase on the platform.
   _____
4 When did you set up your home cinema system?
   _____
5 If you're cold, put your gloves on.
   _____
6 Why have you taken up yoga?
   _____

Vocabulary review

3 Complete the words and phrases related to global issues with the words in the box.

> economic   facts   farming   hunger   increasing
> ~~technology~~   warming   wellbeing

Advances in science and [1] *technology*
The [2] _____ situation
[3] _____ and figures of the financial crisis
Food and [4] _____
Global [5] _____
Health and [6] _____
The [7] _____ population
World [8] _____

4 Complete the words and phrases related to the news with the missing vowels.

[1] *articles*   reach
   crash   [2] r_p_rt
[3] j_ _rn_l_sts   [4] s_c_ _l m_d_ _
[5] n_t_r_l d_s_st_rs   spread
   up to date   [6] w_ _kly

5 Complete the phrasal verbs with the particles in the box. You may use each particle more than once.

> down   on   out   up

1 carry *on* _____ = continue
2 find _____ = discover
3 give _____ = stop
4 grow _____ = get older
5 put _____ = place
6 put _____ = cover something
7 set _____ = start something
8 take _____ = start a hobby

11.4 Speaking and writing

Speaking expressing and responding to opinions

CAM 002

1a Choose the correct option to complete the sentences.

A Beth, what do you think about all the security cameras on the streets today?

B Oh, I ¹ *take /* ⟨*think*⟩ we need them.

A Why's that?

B In my ² *point / view*, they help the police to catch criminals.

A I'm sorry, but I don't really ³ *agree / think*. It's very easy to break the cameras.

B ⁴ *Personally / True*, but what about the criminals who don't know that there's a camera?

A I take your ⁵ *opinion / point*, but the cameras make me feel like a criminal.

B That's ⁶ *OK / right*. It isn't very nice knowing that someone is watching you all the time.

A Exactly. ⁷ *Personally / True*, I don't like it at all.

B ⁸ *I'm sorry / Maybe*. Perhaps there shouldn't be so many of them.

b 11.4))) Listen and check.

2 Complete the conversations with the phrases in the box.

> a good point   ~~I agree~~   I disagree   I don't have
> I don't think   In my opinion   Yeah, but

1 **A** I don't think you should put your personal details on social media.
   B Yeah, _I agree_ .

2 **A** What do you think of modern technology?
   B _____, the world is changing too fast.

3 **A** I think people should pay to download films.
   B I'm afraid _____.

4 **A** Do you think people should stop posting photos on the internet?
   B Not really. _____ strong views on that.

5 **A** You should have a different password for each of your accounts.
   B _____ they're so difficult to remember.

6 **A** What's your opinion of free newspapers?
   B _____ you can believe everything you read.

7 **A** If you use a different name, your friends won't be able to find you.
   B That's _____.

Writing a presentation

3 Rewrite the sentences so that they are suitable for a slide.

1 You shouldn't tell friends your password.
   Never _tell friends your password._

2 No social network is 100% safe.
   Social _____

3 You shouldn't accept friend requests from strangers.
   Do _____

4 You should only chat with your real friends.
   Only _____

5 Don't post your holiday dates on Facebook.
   Do _____

6 You should always log off social media if you leave the room.
   Always _____

I can …	Very well	Quite well	More practice
understand and use phrasal verbs.	○	○	○
express and respond to opinions.	○	○	○
give a presentation.	○	○	○

Work

12.1 The working environment

Vocabulary jobs, professions and workplaces

1 Complete the table with the words in the box.

> building site construction hospital judge laboratory law medical research nurse office personal assistant

Job	Profession	Workplace
builder	¹ *construction*	2 _____
3 _____	4 _____	court
5 _____	health care	6 _____
7 _____	administration	8 _____
scientist	9 _____	10 _____

2 Complete the puzzle with words for jobs, professions and the workplace.

1 A software _____ is a person who designs computer programs.
2 A _____ is a building where goods are made by machines.
3 A _____ is a person who collects and writes about news.
4 _____ is the profession that builds machines and engines or roads and railways.
5 An _____ is a person who organizes a system or manages a business.
6 A _____ is a person who studies subjects like biology, chemistry or physics.
7 An _____ is a person who looks after the finances of a company.
8 _____ is the profession that deals with selling the products of a company.

3 Match the two halves of the sentences.

1 I'm an
2 I'm studying
3 I work as
4 I work for
5 I work
6 I'd like to

a in health care.
b a personal assistant.
c accountant.
d law.
e a construction company.
f become a software developer.

4 Complete the article with the words in the box.

> accountant health care hospital laboratory medical nurse office scientists

When people think about ¹ *scientists* , they often imagine a person in a white coat doing experiments all day in a ² _____. In fact, modern scientists do a lot of different things during their working day, especially if they do ³ _____ research. Some of the researchers have their own ⁴ _____ with a desk and a computer where they can send and receive emails. They have to be in contact with other professionals so that they can share their ideas. Several times a week, they visit a ⁵ _____, where they can study some of the patients. Before they can go, they have to wait for a phone call from a ⁶ _____ who tells them the best time to visit. Of course, scientists need money to be able to do their research. If they work for a company, they have to talk to the ⁷ _____ before they can start a new project. The job of a scientist is very interesting, but it is also really important because they are trying to make ⁸ _____ better for everybody.

Grammar   present perfect simple with *for* and *since*

5a Use the words to write present perfect simple sentences with *for* or *since*.

1   my father / have his car / too long
   My father has had his car for too long.

2   those children / study English / last year
   _____

3   my wife / like the same music / she was a student
   _____

4   my parents / be married / 30 years
   _____

5   John / work as a teacher / he left university
   _____

6   my friends / live in Scotland / six months
   _____

PRONUNCIATION *for* and *since*

b **12.1**))) Listen and check your answers in exercise **5a**. Notice how *have* is pronounced /həv/ and *has* is pronounced /həz/ in the sentences.

c **12.1**))) Listen again. Pause the CD and repeat after each sentence.

6   Use the words to write present perfect questions and answers with *for* or *since*. Use contractions where possible.

1   you / have your current job (seven years)
   A How long *have you had your current job?*
   B *I've had my current job for seven years.*

2   your sister / live abroad (three months)
   A How long _____
   B She _____

3   your parents / work in engineering (they were young)
   A How _____
   B They _____

4   you / know your best friend (ages)
   A _____
   B I _____

5   your partner / be a software developer (he left university)
   A _____
   B He _____

6   your daughter / play the guitar (last year)
   A _____
   B She _____

7 Complete the article with the present perfect of the verbs in the box with *for* or *since*.

be   have   ~~love~~   not speak   use   want

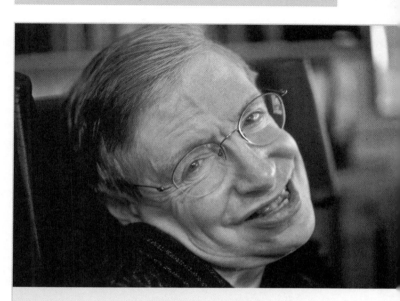

One of the most famous scientists in the world is probably Stephen Hawking. Now in his seventies, the physicist is still fascinated by space and the universe. He **1** _has loved_ science and the sky _since_ he was a child and today he is famous for his research. Stephen Hawking can't work in an office or a laboratory because he is a very ill man. He **2** _____ his illness _____ most of his life, and it means that he can use his mind, but not his body. He isn't able to walk, and he **3** _____ a wheelchair _____ nearly 50 years now. In 1985, he had an important operation and lost his voice forever. He **4** _____ a word _____ the operation, and today he uses a computer program to communicate. Stephen Hawking has been married twice, but he got divorced both times. Now he **5** _____ single _____ about ten years and he spends a lot of time with his children. His daughter, Lucy, helps him write his books. The scientist **6** _____ to travel to space _____ he visited the Kennedy Space Centre in 2007, where he experienced zero gravity. He is hoping to become a space tourist, when the first space flight takes place.

I can ...	Very well	Quite well	More practice
talk about jobs and professions.	○	○	○
use the present perfect simple with *for* and *since*.	○	○	○

12.2 The changing face of work

Vocabulary job responsibilities

1 Circle the verbs that don't go with the words in **bold**.

1 *answer / do / talk on* **the phone**
2 *attend / organize / train* **meetings**
3 *answer / deal with / give* **customer enquiries**
4 *entertain / give / write* **presentations**
5 *employ / recruit / run* **new staff**
6 *advise / entertain / recruit* **clients**
7 *employ / type up / write* **reports**
8 *attend / manage / work in* **a team**

2 Complete the words in the sentences.

1 How many people work in your t_eam_?
2 When was the last time your company recruited new st_____?
3 Who does most of the pa_____ in your office?
4 Where do you go when you have to entertain cl_____?
5 How many m_____ do you have to attend each week?
6 Who deals with customer e_____ in your company?
7 Do you get nervous before you give pr_____?
8 Who runs the day-to-day b_____ of your department?
9 How many e_____ do you receive each day?

3 Complete the article with the correct form of the verbs in the box.

advise   attend   deal with   give   ~~recruit~~   talk on
work in   write

The best job in the world?

Every summer, travel companies **1** _recruit_ people to do one of the best jobs in the world: a water slide tester. This lucky person travels around the world testing all the water slides that belong to the company, making sure that they are safe. The water slide tester **2**_____ a team, but he or she is the only member who works outside of the office. While the others **3**_____ meetings, the water slide tester is busy jumping down a water slide in his or her swimming costume. A water slide tester doesn't have to **4**_____ presentations, but after testing each slide, he or she **5**_____ a short report about its safety. If they think a slide could be dangerous, they call their boss immediately and describe the problem. Together they decide what to **6**_____ the client to do about the slide. Sometimes, they spend hours **7**_____ the phone trying to make the right decision. Later, when the team at home has to **8**_____ enquiries from customers about the slides, they can say there aren't any problems. Water slide testers are important because they keep people safe, but the best thing about the job is that it's fun!

Grammar　uses of the infinitive with *to*

4 Match the two halves of the sentences.

1　Do some research before the interview　　*e*
2　Leave home early and try　　＿＿＿
3　If you're expecting a call, don't forget　　＿＿＿
4　You don't need a pen because it isn't necessary　　＿＿＿
5　Smile, although it's difficult　　＿＿＿
6　Look smart on the day　　＿＿＿

a　not to feel nervous.
b　to turn off your mobile phone.
c　to take notes.
d　to make a good impression.
e　to find out about the company.
f　not to be late.

5a Complete the sentences with the correct form of the verbs in brackets. Use the affirmative or negative form of the verbs.

1　I need _to work_ (work) late because I haven't finished my presentation for tomorrow.
2　Are you going to have a party ＿＿＿＿＿＿ (celebrate) your birthday?
3　It's important ＿＿＿＿＿＿ (say) the wrong thing to your boss.
4　I'll tell you if you promise ＿＿＿＿＿＿ (tell) anybody.
5　Is it easy ＿＿＿＿＿＿ (talk) to your colleagues outside work?
6　It's impossible ＿＿＿＿＿＿ (worry) when your children come home late.
7　Remember ＿＿＿＿＿＿ (call) me when I'm in the meeting.
8　Do you use your phone ＿＿＿＿＿＿ (take) photos?

PRONUNCIATION　*to* in infinitive with *to*

---

b　**12.2**⟩⟩ Listen and check your answers to exercise **5a**. Pay attention to the weak pronunciation /tə/ of *to*.

c　**12.2**⟩⟩ Listen again. Pause the CD and repeat after each sentence.

→ **STUDY TIP** When an infinitive is used with *to*, the pronunciation of *to* is weak /tə/. Practise saying phrases with *to* and *not to* to get the pronunciation right.

6 Complete the article with the correct form of the verbs in the box.

> attend　do　get　give　go　~~have~~　open　return

More than words

Things often go wrong at job interviews and it is quite normal **1** _to have_ a problem. The important thing is your reaction, which can sometimes get you the job. This is exactly what happened to an American woman who was invited **2**＿＿＿＿＿＿ an interview at a company that was looking for a new receptionist. The woman parked outside the building, got out of her car and closed the door quickly … on her thumb! She needed the car keys **3**＿＿＿＿＿＿ the door, but they were in her bag. Eventually, she managed **4**＿＿＿＿＿＿ the keys and open the car door, but her thumb was hurting a lot. She decided **5**＿＿＿＿＿＿ to the interview anyway. She greeted the interviewer, and everything was going well until he asked her **6**＿＿＿＿＿＿ a typing test. She explained that she couldn't do the test because of her accident and she offered **7**＿＿＿＿＿＿ the next day. The interviewer got some ice for her thumb, and asked her a few more questions before she left. The next day she had a call from the company saying that they wanted **8**＿＿＿＿＿＿ her the job. She had been so calm after her accident that they thought she would make an excellent receptionist.

I can …	Very well	Quite well	More practice
talk about what a job involves.	○	○	○
use the infinitive with *to*.	○	○	○

12.3 Vocabulary development

Vocabulary phrases with *in*

1 Replace the words in *italics* with a phrase with *in* and a word in the box.

charge   common   ~~construction~~   detail   hurry   mess   middle   suit   time   trouble

1 You have to be very strong to work *as a builder*.
   in construction

2 My girlfriend and I get on so well because we have a lot *of the same interests*. _____

3 If you're late again, you'll be *asked to speak to the manager*. _____

4 Her brother is the man over there *wearing matching jacket and trousers*. _____

5 She's Head of Human Resources so she's *the person who controls* recruiting new staff. _____

6 I'm going to the bus stop because the bus leaves *five minutes from now*. _____

7 They're *driving very quickly* because they have to go to the airport. _____

8 I'm not surprised you can't find anything. Your room is *untidy* again. _____

9 He completely forgot what he was going to say *during* his speech. _____

10 First you need to make a plan, and then you can write it *with all the facts*. _____

Vocabulary review

2 Complete the table with the words in the box.

~~administrator~~   court   engineering   hospital   judge   law   office   sales   scientist

Jobs	Professions	Workplaces
accountant	administration	building site
1 *administrator*	construction	7 _____
builder	4 _____	factory
journalist	health care	8 _____
2 _____	information technology (IT)	laboratory
nurse	5 _____	9 _____
personal assistant	medical research	
3 _____	politics	
software developer	6 _____	

3 Complete the words with the missing vowels.

Verbs	Nouns
advise / entertain	1 cli**e**nts
answer / deal with	2 _nqu_r_ _s
answer / talk on	3 th_ ph_n_
attend / organize	4 m_ _t_ngs
employ / recruit / train	5 st_ff
give / write	6 pr_s_nt_t_ _ns
manage / work in	a 7 t_ _m

4 Complete the missing vowels in the prepositional phrases with *in*.

fixed phrases
in a mess, 1 *in* det**ai**l, in trouble, 2 _n c_mm_n, in charge of, in a hurry

talking about position or time
3 _n t_n m_n_t_s, in the distance, 4 _n th_ m_ddl_, in five years' time, in front of

talking about a profession
5 _n n_rs_ng, in education, 6 _n s_l_s

wearing something
7 _n _ s_ _t, dressed in black, 8 _n sh_rts

12.4 Speaking and writing

Writing a curriculum vitae (CV)

1 Match headings 1–8 to information a–h.

1	Nationality	a	Drama and Yoga
2	Date of birth	b	Bachelor of Science in Computer Science
3	Email address	c	Business intelligence. Fluent in English and Spanish.
4	Education and qualifications	d	11 May 1987
5	Work experience	e	Portuguese
6	Skills	f	Josie@pmail.pt
7	Interests	g	Paola da Santos, Compufield Lisbon
8	Referee	h	2008–present: Software developer, Compufield Lisbon.

2 Complete the extract from a CV.

Work experience

Technical Director, MH Communications
- ¹ m<u>anaged</u> a team of eight employees
- gave ² tr_____ in programming to new staff
- ³ dev_____ a customer service plan
- ⁴ att_____ courses about new models regularly
- prepared schedules and ⁵ pr_____ weekly reports
- ⁶ ass_____ the management in visiting clients

Skills
- ⁷ fl_____ in English, ⁸ b_____ French,
- good ⁹ kn_____ of most recent equipment

Referees
- on ¹⁰ re_____

Speaking answering questions in a job interview

3a Complete the interview with the phrases in the box.

> I can   I'd really like to get into   I find it hard to
> I'm currently working for   I'm good at
> ~~I've got a university degree in~~   I've worked as a

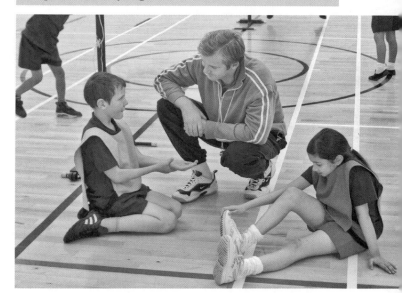

A Robert, what qualifications have you got for this job?
B Well, ¹ _I've got a university degree_ in Sports Management.
A Oh good, and how much experience have you got?
B ² _____ sports centre manager for three years and ³ _____ Pinto Sports near Madrid.
A Right. So why do you want to work for this company?
B I'm enjoying my job right now, but ⁴ _____ community sports.
A Sure. And what are your strengths and weaknesses?
B Strengths? Well, ⁵ _____ dealing with the public, and ⁶ _____ work well in a team. As for weaknesses, ⁷ _____ switch off at the end of the day. But I'm working on that.

b **12.3**))) Listen and check.

I can ...	Very well	Quite well	More practice
understand and use phrases with *in*.	○	○	○
write a CV.	○	○	○
take part in a job interview.	○	○	○

85

12.5 Listening for pleasure

Easter Island statues

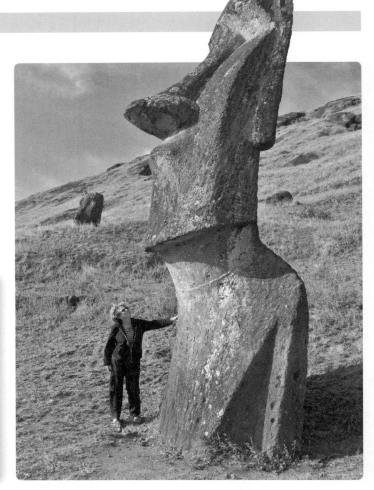

1 Look at the photo of a statue. Match the two halves of the sentences.

1 The statue	a are found on Easter Island.
2 Moais	b is in the South Pacific.
3 Easter Island	c is called a moai.

2 **12.4**))) Listen to a radio documentary about Easter Island and the Rapa Nui people.

3 **12.4**))) Listen again. Choose the correct options to complete the summary.

> There are **1** *787 /* *887* moai on Easter Island. When the Rapa Nui arrived, there were a lot of **2** *statues / trees* on the island. At first life was **3** *easy / difficult* for the Rapa Nui, but everything changed when they started to **4** *make statues / build houses*. They needed wood for **5** *construction / transport*, but in the end, they used too much of it. The Rapa Nui people disappeared because they used all of the **6** *stone / trees* on Easter Island.

4 Think about the story of the Rapa Nui again. Did you find the story surprising. Why/Why not?

Review: Units 11 and 12

Grammar

1 Complete the sentences with the correct form of the verbs in the box.

arrive buy have look after phone stop

1 It's important _to arrive_ on time for a job interview.
2 If we _____ the environment, we wouldn't have as many problems.
3 People used to _____ their friends instead of using social media.
4 We _____ the same boss for many years.
5 Firefighters tried _____ the forest fire before it spread.
6 I _____ an electric car if they were cheaper.

2 Complete the text with one word in each space.

Would you visit Chernobyl **1** _if_ you had the chance? If you went there today, you **2** _____ find a very different city than the one that existed before. Chernobyl **3** _____ use to be famous until its nuclear power plant exploded in 1986. 14,000 people **4** _____ to live in the city, but they all had to leave after the accident. Chernobyl has been empty **5** _____ then, although about 500 residents **6** _____ recently returned to their homes. It isn't easy **7** _____ visit the area, because it is still very dangerous. There is a big fence with a lot of signs warning people **8** _____ to go any further. The only way to enter is on an official tour, but that can be quite expensive.

Vocabulary

3 Match definitions 1–8 to words and phrases in the box.

cure journalist judge reach recruit report

1 a person who writes articles for a newspaper _journalist_
2 arrive at a place _____
3 treatment that can make somebody healthy again _____
4 give people information about something that has happened _____
5 find new people for a job _____
6 a person who has to decide how to punish a criminal _____

4 Complete the words in the text.

The job market is not looking good these days, and it's pretty clear that **1** u_nemployment_ is likely to rise in the future. **2** A_____ in science and technology mean that machines and robots have taken many of the jobs that humans used to do. So which jobs are likely to exist and which will disappear? There may be less work in **3** c_____ soon because of new techniques in 3D printing. On the other hand, there will be more posts for **4** s_____ d_____, because computers will be more important in our lives. In **5** h_____ c_____, we will still need **6** n_____ to look after patients because this is something that machines can't do. But there will probably be fewer jobs in **7** a_____ because a new generation of office robots will do all the **8** p_____.

5 Choose the correct option to complete the sentences.
1 Why do children *grow up* / *set up* so quickly?
2 Who is *in the middle of* / *in charge of* recruiting new staff in your company?
3 How much do you have *in trouble* / *in common* with your colleagues?
4 How long do you think you will *put down* / *carry on* working before you can retire?
5 Do you keep your desk tidy or is it usually *in detail* / *in a mess*?
6 Where can I *find out* / *put on* more about global warming?

Speaking

6 Put the words in the correct order to make sentences.
1 sorry, / agree / I / but / don't / I'm / really
   I'm sorry, but I don't really agree.
2 currently / company / an / working / I'm / for / IT
   _____
3 really / sales / to / I'd / get / like / into
   _____
4 not / opinion, / exist / world / should / my / In / hunger
   _____
5 strong / have / media / the / views / don't / on / I
   _____
6 in / it / work / hard / I / team / find / to / a
   _____

Audioscripts

Unit 1 Time

Page 5, Exercises 4b & c

1.1 🔊

1
A   What time do you get up during the week?
B   At half past seven.

2
A   Who is the first person you see every morning?
B   My brother. He gets up at the same time as me.

3
A   Where do you have breakfast?
B   In the kitchen.

4
A   How much coffee do you drink?
B   I have three or four cups a day.

5
A   When do you stop for lunch?
B   From one o'clock until two.

6
A   How often do you eat in a restaurant?
B   About twice a month.

7
A   How many good friends do you have?
B   A lot. I have a lot of good friends.

8
A   What kind of car do you drive?
B   I drive a Mini.

Page 5, Exercises 5b & c

1.2 🔊

1   When is your birthday?
2   Who do you chat with online?
3   What kind of films do you like?
4   Are you busy right now?
5   How often do you spend time with relatives?
6   How many hours did you sleep last night?
7   Where are you from?
8   Did you go shopping yesterday?

Page 6, Exercises 1b & c

1.3 🔊

1   They often go out for a coffee.
2   My girlfriend goes running every now and then.

3   We don't usually go camping in the summer.
4   My best friend does aerobics once or twice a week.
5   I hardly ever play computer games.
6   My family don't often make future plans.

Page 9, Exercises 2b & c

1.4 🔊

1   I love going clubbing.
2   I can't stand the winter.
3   I'm really into yoga.
4   My favourite sport is basketball.
5   I don't mind doing housework.
6   I'm not keen on thunderstorms.
7   I quite like going camping.
8   I prefer football to golf.
9   I'm really interested in doing karate.

Unit 2 Inside outside

Page 10, Exercises 4b & c

2.1 🔊

1	cleaner	6	pedestrian
2	crowded	7	performer
3	lively	8	rubbish
4	market	9	souvenir
5	pavement	10	statue

Page 11, Exercises 5b & c

2.2 🔊

1   We're tired. We're having an early night.
2   My husband is late for work. He's running out of the door.
3   You can turn the TV off. I'm not watching it.
4   Your dog is hungry. It's waiting by the cupboard.
5   Can you help me? I'm doing my English homework.
6   My parents are angry. They aren't talking to each other.
7   Robert is in bed. He isn't feeling very well.
8   My grandfather is 80 today. We're celebrating his birthday with him.

Page 12, Exercises 4b & c

2.3 🔊

1   It's something that you have in your house.
2   It's something that you turn on and off.
3   It's something that has water in it.

Page 15, Exercise 1b

2.4 🔊

A   Please could you tell us how to get to the town hall?
B   Yes, go straight down here, cross the road at the lights and take the second left.
A   Can you show us on the map?
B   Yes, here it is. You can't miss it.
A   OK, so it's down here and second left after the lights?
B   That's right. It takes about ten minutes.
A   Thanks.

Unit 3 Going up, going down

Page 19, Exercises 5b & c

3.1 🔊

1   dived   dropped   jumped   landed
2   booked   climbed   lifted   walked
3   arrived   travelled   turned   wanted
4   asked   looked   waited   worked
5   called   painted   played   listened
6   danced   helped   started   watched

Page 20, Exercises 1c & d

3.2 🔊

One syllable:
calm, pleased, scared, stressed

Two syllables:
anxious, confused, guilty, lonely, nervous

Three syllables:
embarrassed, excited, exhausted

Four syllables:
disappointed

Page 23, Exercise 1b

3.3 🔊

Conversation 1
A   We had a bad experience when we were on holiday a few years ago. We hired a car and went exploring on the coast.
B   Where were you?

A In the Canary Islands – in Fuerteventura, to be exact. So, anyway, we were in this hired car and we decided to leave the main road. We were driving in some sand when, suddenly, the car got stuck.

B Oh no!

A That's what I thought. I was so angry with my husband – he went right when I said left, and suddenly, we were lost and stuck.

B So, what did you do?

A We walked about five kilometres to the nearest road, and then we got a taxi back to our hotel, where we called for help. It was all OK in the end, but it cost us €250 to get the car out of the sand!

Conversation 2

A A funny thing happened last weekend when we went for a walk. We parked our car in a pretty little village and walked over the mountains to the next village. We were hoping to get a bus back to our car.

B So, what happened?

A We asked in a café about the buses, but there weren't any.

B You're joking!

A No, it's true. The café was full, so we left and started looking for a place to have lunch. We were walking along the road when a woman stopped her car and told us to get in.

B Why did she do that?

A She heard us ask about the buses in the café, so she knew where we wanted to go. You see, she was working in the village where our car was, and so she took us there on the way to work. We were so pleased!

Unit 4 Changes and challenges

Page 25, Exercises 6a & b

4.1 》))

1 When did you learn to drive?
2 What did you decide to wear?
3 Who did you want to win?
4 How much did you plan to spend?
5 Where would you like to go?
6 Why did you need to stop?

Page 26, Exercise 2b

4.2 》))

1
A What do you do when you're feeling lonely?
B I text friends. They always make me feel better.

2
A What's the first thing you do on Monday mornings?
B I deal with emails. I usually have hundreds to answer.

3
A Do you ever buy a newspaper?
B No, I read the news on the internet.

4
A Where do you pay your electricity bill?
B On the internet. I do online banking so I don't have to leave my house.

5
A How often do you use social media?
B A lot. But you don't need to update your Facebook page every day – you can add photos and comments when you like.

6
A How did you listen to that song?
B On my mobile phone. I often download music from the internet.

7
A Have you got a digital camera?
B No, I use my phone because it's easier to share photos with my friends.

8
A Are you worried about internet security?
B Not really. I never post personal information on a website.

Page 29, Exercises 1b & c

4.3 》))

A Are you doing anything at the weekend?
B I'm working on Saturday, but I'm free on Sunday.
A Do you fancy going to the Renoir exhibition at the Prado?
B Yeah, I'd love to.
A Shall we meet outside the museum when it opens?
B I'm afraid I can't go that early, because I'm playing tennis. Could we meet in the afternoon instead?
A Sure. Is two o'clock OK for you?
B Two o'clock is perfect. See you there.

Page 30, Exercises 2 & 3

4.4 》))

P = Presenter, A = Amy

P It takes a long time to build a house, and the end result is usually very expensive, as you know if you're trying to buy one. But a Chinese company has found a fantastic new way to make houses that are cheap AND take less time to build. Amy Chang is here to tell us all about them. Amy, how are the houses made?

A Well, believe it or not, they are made by a 3D computer printer.

P A computer printer! You're joking!

A No, I'm not. It's true. But this computer printer is no ordinary printer. It's absolutely huge. The printer is 150 metres long and ten metres wide. It doesn't print the finished house, but it prints the different parts of it. Then, workers have to put the parts together to make the house.

P But what is the house made of? It obviously isn't paper!

A No, no. The house is made of concrete. But the interesting thing is that the company is using recycled waste to make the concrete. The waste comes from building and industry and the company needs a lot of it to make the houses. That's why they're going to build a hundred new factories in China to recycle the waste.

P So the houses are green as well as cheap and easy to build. Amy, what does a printed house look like?

A Well, these houses are much smaller than normal ones and they only have one floor. But you can have a window if you want, and you can divide the house into two rooms. It depends on the design, really.

P And what about the price? How much does one of these printed houses cost?

A Each one costs around 3,650 euros. But you have to go to China to buy one. Actually, the houses aren't really for people like you and me. They are really for people without a home. Perhaps they are too poor to buy a house or maybe they have lost their home in a natural disaster. The company that makes them, the WinSun Decoration Design Engineering Company, has spent years working on the houses – and the printer.

P Well, I think it's a great idea! Amy Chang, thank you for joining us.

Unit 5 Stuff and things

Page 32, Exercises 4b & c

5.1 》)

1	useful	5	special
2	heavy	6	antique
3	leather	7	plastic
4	metal	8	tiny

Page 34, Exercises 1a & b

5.2 》)

1 bag
2 note
3 bill
4 purse
5 credit card
6 wallet

Page 37, Exercise 1b

5.3 》)

A Good morning. Are you looking for anything in particular?
B Oh, hello. Yes, I am, but I don't know the word in English.
A Well, can you describe it for me?
B Yes, it's a thing that you use to keep warm in the winter.
A Is it something you wear?
B No, it looks like a carpet, but it's smaller.
A And do you put it on the floor?
B That's right. Do you know what I mean?
A Yes, I do. It's a rug. Come with me and I'll show you where they are.

Unit 6 People

Page 38, Exercises 3b & c

6.1 》)

1 clever honest lazy patient
2 confident sociable
3 creative untidy

Page 40, Exercises 4b & c

6.2 》)

1 son mother adopt
2 aunt father parent
3 divorced cousin uncle
4 daughter engaged sister-in-law
5 couple husband only

Unit 7 Travel

Page 47, Exercises 5a & b

7.1 》)

I might buy a car.
I might buy a car.

Page 47, Exercise 5c

7.2 》)

1 I might go to Canada this year.
2 She might take you to the station.
3 You might get a seat.
4 It might rain later.
5 We might catch the train if we run.

Page 48, Exercises 4b & c

7.3 》)

1 book your flight
2 lie by the pool
3 try the local food
4 hire a car
5 read a guidebook
6 apply for a visa
7 go sightseeing
8 explore the area

Page 51, Exercise 1b

7.4 》)

A Hi, I'd like to check in, please.
B Yes, of course. Do you have a reservation?
A Yes, my name's Tatiana Genieva.
B OK, Ms Genieva. So that's a single room just for one night?
A Yeah, that's right.
B Could you fill in the registration form, please?
A Yeah, sure. Just one question. What time is check-out?
B You have to vacate your room by 10.30.
A Right. Is there anywhere I can leave my luggage tomorrow?
B Yes, you can leave it behind reception.
A Thanks a lot.

Unit 8 Language and learning

Page 52, Exercises 1b & c

8.1 》)

1 My sister isn't able to walk because she has broken her leg.
2 Are you able to lend me some money to go to a concert?
3 I'm able to drive but I haven't got a car.
4 We're able to see the sea from the window of our room.

5 Is your boyfriend able to speak any foreign languages?
6 I'm tired because I'm not able to sleep at night.

Page 55, Exercises 4a & b

8.2 》)

1 You can use the internet.
2 You can't take photos.
3 You can sit here.
4 You can't walk on the grass.
5 You can pay by credit card.
6 You can't play football here.

Page 57, Exercise 2b

8.3 》)

A = Amara, R = Raz

A Raz? Where are you?
R Hi, Amara. I'm on my way.
A Pardon?
R I'm on my way.
A Sorry, it's too noisy in here. Are you on your way? The party started an hour ago.
R Amara, I'm nearly there. But I've forgotten your address.
A Sorry, Raz. You're breaking up. Can you remember my address?
R No, that's the problem.
A Raz, please could you speak up?
R OK. IS THAT BETTER?
A Yes, that's much better. I said can you remember my address? It's number 107.
R Could you repeat that, please?
A 1-0-7. A hundred and seven South View Avenue.
R Right. Please could you explain how to get there from the bus stop?
A OK. When you get off the bus, walk up the hill and take the second right.
R Amara, this is a really bad connection.
A Up the hill and second right. Did you get that?
R Sorry, I'm a bit lost …
A Raz. Raz? He's gone.

Page 58, Exercises 2 & 3

8.4 》)

Speaker 1
This happened on a car journey we did one spring – to the village where my mother-in-law lives. We decided to drive over the mountains, but it started to snow, and soon there was ice and snow everywhere. We had to drive very slowly and there were a lot of cars at the side of the road. Fortunately, my husband is a very good driver, so we got there in the end.

Speaker 2
I had a very bad experience one night when I was riding home on my bike. I had my lights on and everything, but that didn't seem to make any difference. I came to a roundabout where I wanted to go straight on, but suddenly this lorry appeared. It crossed over right in front of me – it was so close that it touched my foot. I don't know how I didn't fall off my bike!

Speaker 3
I was in a hotel once and I couldn't sleep. I got up to look out of the window, and I saw some big black clouds in the sky. Only they weren't clouds, and I suddenly realized that there was a fire – in my hotel! I didn't know what to do. Luckily, the emergency services were already there, and somebody came to take me outside. What a nightmare!

Speaker 4
I've never been very keen on flying, but my last trip was worse than ever. The weather was awful, and it was really cloudy, so the pilot was having problems landing. The plane was moving all over the place, and everybody was holding on to their seats. We tried to land three times before we actually stopped going up in the air again. It was very frightening, I can tell you.

Speaker 5
I had a really frightening experience on a train once. A man got on the train and sat down opposite me. We got talking, and to start with, he seemed really nice. Then he told me to give him my mobile phone. Of course, I said no, but then he started shouting at me and I was really frightened because there weren't many people around. I gave him my phone in the end, and he got off at the next station with it.

Speaker 6
My most frightening experience was when I nearly drowned. I was swimming in the sea off the coast of Mauritius about four years ago and suddenly I couldn't stand in the water and the sea was moving me away from my friends and I couldn't get back to them. One friend saw what was happening and said, 'Don't panic! Just wait until the current brings you back!' And luckily it did. But I never went in the sea again on that holiday!

Speaker 7
I was very frightened about six weeks ago when my six-year-old son had problems while he was eating dinner. He had been eating steak and put a large piece into his mouth and then tried to eat it but it was stuck and he couldn't breathe! His face became red and he didn't know what to do and neither did I. Fortunately my sister was in the house and she hit him on the back, then the piece of meat came out. But we were all very frightened and we cried a lot.

Unit 9 Body and mind

Page 61, Exercises 6a & b
9.1))
1	I'll	5	She'll
2	You'll	6	We'll
3	It'll	7	They'll
4	He'll		

Page 62, Exercises 4b & c
9.2))
1	eat	read
2	bread	meat
3	disease	dream
4	easy	weather
5	health	leather
6	already	instead
7	breakfast	team
8	cleaner	pleased

Page 65, Exercise 2b
9.3))
A Morning. How can I help you?
B Hello. Have you got anything for a cold?
A Well, there isn't much I can do really. I think you should go home and get lots of rest.
B Can you give me something for my cough? It's very annoying.
A Yes, you could try this medicine. Take it every six hours until the cough goes away.
B Right.
A It's a good idea to drink lots of water, too. And keep warm. You mustn't go out.
B OK. Thank you very much.

Unit 10 Food

Page 67, Exercises 4b & c
10.1))
Two-syllable words:
chocolate
different
favourite
raspberry
restaurant
several
strawberry

Three-syllable words:
interesting
temperature
vegetable

Page 68, Exercise 2b
10.2))
four tins of chicken soup
six packets of sausages
two bottles of ketchup
two tubes of tomato paste
three jars of olives
two boxes of strawberries
four cartons of cream
sixteen cans of drinks

Page 71, Exercise 2b
10.3))
Conversation 1
A Excuse me? I'm afraid I can't eat this steak. It's raw.
B Really? I'll take it back to the kitchen for you.
A No, I'd like to order something else, please.
B Of course. What would you like?
A I'm not sure. Would you mind bringing me the menu again?
B Of course not. I'm terribly sorry about your steak.
A Don't worry about it. Erm, I'll have a salad, please.
Conversation 2
A Excuse me? Could you possibly bring me the bill?
B Yes, of course … Here it is.
A Oh. There seems to be a mistake.
B Is there?
A Yes. You've charged me for the steak, but I didn't eat it.
B You're absolutely right. I do apologize.
A Don't worry. It's not your fault.

Unit 11 World

Page 75, Exercise 4b

11.1 》)

1 If I had a car, I would drive to work.

Page 75, Exercises 4c & d

11.2 》)

2 I wouldn't be happy if I lost my job.
3 What would you do if you could go back in time?
4 If she knew his number, she'd call him.
5 Where would you live if you had the choice?
6 You'd feel better if you did some exercise.

Page 76, Exercise 1b

11.3 》)

1 My brother used to work in a bank.
2 We didn't use to have a garden.
3 My parents used to live in a flat.
4 Did you use to have long hair?
5 I didn't use to drink coffee.
6 Did your boyfriend use to have a motorbike?
7 I used to wear glasses.

Page 79, Exercise 1b

11.4 》)

A Beth, what do you think about all the security cameras on the streets today?
B Oh, I think we need them.
A Why's that?
B In my view, they help the police to catch criminals.
A I'm sorry, but I don't really agree. It's very easy to break the cameras.
B True, but what about the criminals who don't know that there's a camera?
A I take your point, but the cameras make me feel like a criminal.
B That's right. It isn't very nice knowing that someone is watching you all the time.
A Exactly. Personally, I don't like it at all.
B Maybe. Perhaps there shouldn't be so many of them.

Unit 12 Work

Page 81, Exercises 5b & c

12.1 》)

1 My father has had his car for too long.
2 Those children have studied English since last year.
3 My wife has liked the same music since she was a student.

4 My parents have been married for 30 years.
5 John has worked as a teacher since he left university.
6 My friends have lived in Scotland for six months.

Page 83, Exercises 5b & c

12.2 》)

1 I need to work late because I haven't finished my presentation for tomorrow.
2 Are you going to have a party to celebrate your birthday?
3 It's important not to say the wrong thing to your boss.
4 I'll tell you if you promise not to tell anybody.
5 Is it easy to talk to your colleagues outside work?
6 It's impossible not to worry when your children come home late.
7 Remember not to call me when I'm in the meeting.
8 Do you use your phone to take photos?

Page 85, Exercise 3b

12.3 》)

A Robert, what qualifications have you got for this job?
B Well, I've got a university degree in Sports Management.
A Oh good, and how much experience have you got?
B I've worked as a sports centre manager for three years and I'm currently working for Pinto Sports near Madrid.
A Right. So why do you want to work for this company?
B I'm enjoying my job right now, but I'd really like to get into community sports.
A Sure. And what are your strengths and weaknesses?
B Strengths? Well, I'm good at dealing with the public, and I can work well in a team. As for weaknesses, I find it hard to switch off at the end of the day. But I'm working on that.

Page 86, Exercises 2 & 3

12.4 》)

Presenter: There is an island in the South Pacific, about 3,600 km from the coast of Chile, called Easter Island. It isn't huge, and it doesn't have any tall trees, but it has a lot of massive stone statues on it

called *moai*. Most of the moai are over nine metres tall, and there are 887 of them in total. They were created between the years 1250 and 1500 by the people who lived there: the Rapa Nui.

The Rapa Nui arrived at Easter Island from across the sea in large wooden boats. At the time, the island was covered with very tall trees, and it was the perfect place to live. They used the wood from the trees to build houses and new boats to go fishing. There was more than enough food for everybody and the population grew. Soon, some people went to live in different parts of the island. Then, the Rapa Nui started to make statues. Nobody is sure of the reason for these statues, but some people say that one was made each time an important leader died. The statues were all made in the same place, and then they were transported across the island. Trees were cut down to transport the statues, and as more statues were made, more trees were cut down. In the end, the Rapa Nui cut down all of the trees on the island. This was a disaster. Now, there were no trees to protect the land, so they could not grow any plants, and they had no wood to make boats to go fishing. Soon, there was not enough food for everybody. People started fighting, and the Rapa Nui began to die of hunger. The population fell from 15,000 to around 750. It was the beginning of the end of the Rapa Nui.

Today, the only thing that remains of the Rapa Nui on Easter Island is the moai. But their story can teach us a valuable lesson. On such a small island, it was easy to see what was happening as the trees disappeared. But the people carried on cutting them down. The rest of us can learn from the Rapa Nui. We have already seen the natural disasters that happen when we don't look after the planet. But there is still time to save it. If we start taking more interest in the environment, the same thing that happened to the Rapa Nui may not happen to us.

Irregular verbs

Infinitive	Past simple	Past participle
be	was/were	been
become	became	become
begin	began	begun
break	broke	broken
bring	brought	brought
build	built	built
buy	bought	bought
can	could	been able to
catch	caught	caught
choose	chose	chosen
come	came	come
cost	cost	cost
cut	cut	cut
do	did	done
drink	drank	drunk
drive	drove	driven
eat	ate	eaten
fall	fell	fallen
feel	felt	felt
fight	fought	fought
find	found	found
fly	flew	flown
forget	forgot	forgotten
freeze	froze	frozen
get	got	got
give	gave	given
go	went	gone/been
grow	grew	grown
have	had	had
hear	heard	heard
hit	hit	hit
keep	kept	kept
know	knew	known
learn	learnt/learned	learnt/learned
leave	left	left

Infinitive	Past simple	Past participle
lend	lent	lent
let	let	let
lose	lost	lost
make	made	made
meet	met	met
pay	paid	paid
put	put	put
read	read	read
ride	rode	ridden
ring	rang	rung
run	ran	run
say	said	said
see	saw	seen
sell	sold	sold
send	sent	sent
shut	shut	shut
sing	sang	sung
sit	sat	sat
sleep	slept	slept
speak	spoke	spoken
spend	spent	spent
stand	stood	stood
steal	stole	stolen
swim	swam	swum
take	took	taken
teach	taught	taught
tell	told	told
think	thought	thought
throw	threw	thrown
understand	understood	understood
wake	woke	woken
wear	wore	worn
win	won	won
write	wrote	written

Phonemic symbols

Single vowel sounds

/iː/	tree /triː/	/ə/	computer /kəmˈpjuːtə/
/ɪ/	his /hɪz/	/ɜː/	learn /lɜːn/
/i/	happy /ˈhæpi/	/ɔː/	four /fɔː/
/ʊ/	good /gʊd/	/æ/	hat /hæt/
/u/	usual /ˈjuːʒuəl/	/ʌ/	sunny /ˈsʌni/
/uː/	school /skuːl/	/ɑː/	car /kɑː/
/e/	ten /ten/	/ɒ/	clock /klɒk/

Consonant sounds

/p/	pen /pen/	/s/	see /siː/
/b/	big /bɪg/	/z/	lazy /ˈleɪzi/
/t/	tea /tiː/	/ʃ/	shower /ˈʃaʊə/
/d/	do /duː/	/ʒ/	television /ˈtelɪvɪʒn/
/tʃ/	children /ˈtʃɪldrən/	/m/	man /mæn/
/dʒ/	journey /ˈdʒɜːni/	/n/	never /ˈnevə/
/k/	cat /kæt/	/ŋ/	sing /sɪŋ/
/g/	go /gəʊ/	/h/	hot /hɒt/
/f/	fly /flaɪ/	/l/	like /laɪk/
/v/	very /ˈveri/	/r/	river /ˈrɪvə/
/θ/	thing /θɪŋ/	/w/	water /ˈwɔːtə/
/ð/	this /ðɪs/	/j/	yes /jes/

Diphthongs (double vowel sounds)

/ɪə/	near /nɪə/	/ɔɪ/	boy /bɔɪ/
/ʊə/	tour /tʊə/	/aɪ/	try /traɪ/
/eə/	wear /weə/	/əʊ/	so /səʊ/
/eɪ/	train /treɪn/	/aʊ/	out /aʊt/

Great Clarendon Street, Oxford, OX2 6DP, United Kingdom

Oxford University Press is a department of the University of Oxford.
It furthers the University's objective of excellence in research, scholarship,
and education by publishing worldwide. Oxford is a registered trade
mark of Oxford University Press in the UK and in certain other countries

ACKNOWLEDGEMENTS

The publisher would like to thank the following for permission to reproduce photographs:
Alamy Images pp.5 (women/Ken Weingart), 7 (nightclub/Lou Linwei), 9 (tea
leaf/yu liang wong), 12 (Gojohaven/Horizons WWP), 15 (colleagues/PhotoAlto),
16 (wastewater pipes/Robert Brook), 17 (Egypt cruise ship/Hemis), 19 (Yuri
Gagarin/Heritage Image Partnership Ltd), 27 (Pregnant woman/Stockbroker),
27 (Plane taking off/Eric Gevaert), 30 (Semi detached house/Paul Thompson
Images), 31 (Houdini/Mary Evans Picture Library), 32 (old TV/Judith Collins),
32 (plasma TV/Tony Cordoza), 34 (bill/D. Hurst), 34 (credit card/incamerastock),
37 (couple shopping/Kzenon), 38 (women in burqa/Alan Gignoux), 40 (smiling
woman/MBI), 40 (brother & sister/Wave Royalty Free/Design Pics Inc), 41 (male
driver/Denis Rozhnovsky), 45 (Aung San Suu Kyi/Homer Sykes), 47 (Mars/
PF-(space1)), 55 (elevator/Dinodia Photos), 57 (woman at club/ImageDB),
65 (pharmacist/Blend Images), 72 (cacao fruit/Bon Appetit), 79 (chatting/
Bill Lyons), 81 (Professor Stephen Hawking), 83 (woman with plaster/Radius
Images), 86 (Easter Island/M. Timothy O'Keefe), 86 (Moai statues/John Elk III);
Corbis p.13 (kitchen/Justin Paget/Tetra Images); Getty Images pp.7 (exercise
class/Blake Little), 13 (towel/sinankocaslan), 13 (dirty dish cloth/Erkki
Makkonen), 13 (wardrobe/Richard Wheatley), 22 (jogging/SelectStock), 24 (Bill
Gates/Chesnot), 25 (Tired woman in office/Bodil Johansson), 27 (Skydiver/
Joe McBride), 27 (Couple shopping/LdF), 27 (Groom checking watch/Brand X
Pictures), 28 (Couple waking to tennis courts/Image Source), 28 (Wedding ring
exchange/Eric Larrayadieu), 29 (El Prado Museum/PNC), 33 (Voyager 1/The
LIFE Picture Collection), 42 (eccentric woman/Chris Aschenbrener), 51 (check
in/Shalom Ormsby), 53 (speaker/Ghislain & Marie David de Lossy), 54 (Indian
schoolchildren/AFP), 58 (roundabout/James Morgan), 58 (snowy road/
Tetra Images-Johannes Kroemer), 61 (flatmates/Westend61), 68 (flatmates/
Franek Strzeszewski), 68 (Loren Shriver/Space Frontiers), 76 (female anchor/
ColorBlind Images), 82 (water slide/Justin Lewis); iStockphoto pp.13 (carpet/
zxcynosure), 13 (mirror/emesilva), 13 (clothesline/MartynaPiorek), 13 (duvet/
NAKphotos); Oxford University Press pp.16 (cover), 34 (ten dollars/Westend61),
44 (cover), 50 (Eiffel Tower/Eike Van de Velde), 72 (cover), 85 (PE/Gareth Boden);
Press Association Images pp.21 (Larry Walters/Randy Mudrick/AP), 44 (Civil
Rights Integration 1957/William p. Straeter/AP); Shutterstock pp.4 (jogger/
wavebreakmedia), 7 (basketball/AstroStar), 7 (woman on laptop/Aaron Amat),
7 (gym/wavebreakmedia), 7 (playing cards/racorn), 7 (yoga/East), 7 (camping/
wavebreakmedia), 10 (Marrakesh/Kemal Taner), 11 (Barcelona/Liudmila
Ermolenko), 18 (bull/Stefanie Mohr Photography), 19 (earth/Denis Tabler),
20 (sad boy/RimDream), 23 (stuck car/Piotr Sikora), 34 (wallet/mrHanson),
34 (purse/Timof), 34 (bag/Elnur), 35 (parking meter/Dmitry Kalinovsky),
39 (fruit salad/margouillat photo), 46 (Mayakovskaya metro station/d13),
48 (shopping/emberiza), 49 (Krakow/De Visu), 53 (mechanic/wavebreakmedia),
53 (class/Monkey Business Images), 53 (doctor/pkchai), 58 (airplane/Ondrej
Zabransky), 58 (fire/James Steidl), 60 (man/Kiko Calderon ESP), 62 (veg/
cooperr), 63 (stretching/Robert Kneschke), 64 (open living room/smoxx),
66 (zucchini tart/zi3000), 66 (tiramisu/cobraphotography), 66 (sushi/Ostancov
Vladislav), 66 (green curry/Sommai), 67 (chef/wavebreakmedia), 69 (pizza/
svry), 70 (tomato/S-F), 70 (garlic.Peter Zijlstra), 70 (cucumber/Gosia McCurdy),
70 (onions/S1001), 71 (fish icon/Anthonycz), 74 (refinery/Kodda), 75 (cow/
Sebastian Knight), 77 (tropical storm/B747), 77 (voting/Ververidis Vasilis),
77 (protest/Eric Crama), 77 (forest fire/Ruslan Absurdov), 77 (flood/paintings),
77 (theft/Syda Productions), 78 (kayaking/kuznetcov_konstantin), 84 (cement/
Zurijeta).